Book Reviews

"The incorporation of Lean into a Safe Workplace book is very positive and powerful. An organised workplace is a safer one and Gavin clearly identifies ways and means to achieve this in his book"
— *Professor Mr Richard Keegan Trinity Business School*

Workplace safety on a budget provides an excellent "how-to" guide for small to medium size enterprises seeking insights into providing a safe working environment. With an extensive range of topics, related to business processes, software aids, and safety practices, the book is crammed with practical knowledge of basic OSH requirements in simple and easy to understand language. The book nicely balances a strategic overview of how to plan and implement OSH, while discussing the nuts and bolts of delivering safety. Providing many useful practical insights, Gavin discusses both the pros and cons of various courses of action, leveraging his extensive experience in the business and safety world. A worthwhile read for busy managers, safety professionals, or anyone else concerned with improving their workplace safety.

—*Mr Dom Cooper CEO B-Safe Management Solutions*

WORK PLACE
SAFETY
ON A BUDGET

How to stop and prevent
accidents and injuries
without sacrificing
the bottom line

GAVIN COYLE

For more information, email gavin@gavin-coyle.com

ISBN: 979-8-88759-390-6

Lead Magnet

Thank you very much for purchasing our book. We hope you enjoy it and get some key learning outcomes.

In order to help you along your safety journey we have also created an online Health & Safety course that is a MUST DO for any safety professional or business owner. The course has been created by Gavin and his safety experts team and is a great resource for anybody looking to create a safe working environment for their people.

Our Risk Assessment online course is usually €27.99 cent, but as you have purchased this book we are offering this course to you for €0.99 cent. Just use the QR code provided here and follow the instructions to get access to the online course.

Let's work together to stay safe together!

Dedication

This Book is dedicated to my wife Ashling and my Kids Leah and Emily. They have always been a source of support, encouragement and grounding for me. Thanks guys!

Contents

Introduction

Workplace safety is critical for all businesses, as a safer business will be easier to operate. A business will be more efficient when everyone is protected and at a low risk of harm. Everyone will also feel more motivated because they know they won't have to worry about anything wrong happening to them while on the job.

But efforts to make businesses safe can be challenging to implement, as not all groups have the assets necessary to implement safety plans. Sometimes the worry arises from money, as businesses often assume they require high budgets to plan workplace safety programs.

Many people are concerned about how expensive safety training and planning can be. They might be worried about the materials necessary for training and being compliant. Money is tight for many businesses, and it can be a challenge to manage.

But today's businesses can handle workplace safety projects without breaking their budgets. This guide will cover various tasks surrounding how you can manage a workplace safety program while on a budget.

You will learn how to prepare a workplace safety plan based on how to train people, hire consultants, and use various procedures in your business. Part of the work includes using freelance employees, implementing lean processes, and looking at safety marketing and software programs that fit your business. Other alternative ways of operating your business are also included in this guide, with many of them helping you save money in the process.

This guide will help you review how you can plan your business based on your objectives and current assets. You will see how you can use what you have to plan a workplace safety program that fits your needs and protects your employees.

Many of the practices you will discover are efforts that have been used by various entities in the past. They employ these solutions to improve how well they can operate while saving money. These measures show it is possible to spend less and still maintain workplace safety.

Some of these efforts are also preventative. By preventing injuries and other threats, you will reduce the risk of spending money on insurance claims, worker's compensation, and other expenses that come with injuries. Your business will also be more efficient, as people will remain at work and feel more confident in how the work environment operates. The potential to be fined for infractions will also become minimal.

There are also multiple specifics involved with workplace safety to explore in this guide. These include concepts on how to handle falls, hazardous materials, first aid, and many other aspects without spending more money than needed. Every safety opportunity has different options to find, but the cost for some items may be too high. You'll have to review what you need for specific situations and the likelihood of certain problems occurring. Your planning can help you see what is right for your business while being available within your budget.

The expenses associated with not being safe are too dramatic to ignore. You could struggle with injuries, lawsuits, legal violations, and other problems.

The National Safety Council writes that in 2020, an average business lost about $1,100 for each worker injury. The loss goes up to $44,000 for medically-consulted injuries, as these injuries are often more severe and require more care alongside more time lost.

The NSC also says businesses can lose even more money from workplace deaths. A business will lose about $1.3 million per worker death due to the need to completely replace an employee, the need to cover life insurance and final expenses, and any possible legal actions or fines that might occur.

These expenses are hard to manage and can be costly, which makes keeping a safe workplace up and running all the more essential. Planning a safety routine is critical to keeping your business safe, and the points here will keep you from losing all that money. But you won't spend lots of money to get these plans implemented either.

The details in this guide are simple, but they are also critical to understand. Your business will require a thorough safety plan that fits your needs and works for everyone. This guide will educate you on seeing how you can create a protective and positive work environment for all while staying within your budget.

Disclaimer

This guide includes general details on enhancing workplace safety without spending more than necessary. The details follow general recommendations and ideas. These points are suitable for most industries.

All states and territories have different laws and standards for workplace safety. Be sure when planning your safety efforts that you're doing so based on the rules in your local area or industry.

All materials and procedures listed in this guide are designed for workplace safety. Be sure to follow all instructions as necessary and use your best judgment in all situations.

The producers of this guide cannot be held responsible for any injuries or harm that may occur due to the improper use of information in this book.

Unless listed otherwise, all prices listed in this guide are in American Dollars.

1

Safety Planning

When was the last time you took a look at your business' safety measures? The odds are you might not have thought about your safety needs as much as you should.

You may figure everyone in the workplace is safe enough, and there's no need to worry about what others are doing. But there's no guarantee the worksite will always be this secure. You might come across some sudden threats in the workplace that may be dangerous.

Health and safety threats can happen at any time and without warning. A new machine or procedure may require some changes in the workplace that make it harder for your business to operate. People may struggle to get used to those changes, making the workplace riskier. New safety standards may also be hard for people to manage, especially as some might be more used to older standards for work.

Preparing for these problems before they can become worse is vital to your success. Your business must have a suitable safety plan to ensure everyone in your workplace is protected and not at risk of potential harm. You'll need to look at the risks in your workplace and prepare to manage whatever issues may appear.

Every business has unique risks it needs to manage to stay safe. You can check your risks and use them to determine the needs your business has for keeping safe. This effort helps you figure out how much work you need to put into workplace safety, plus it gives you an idea of what you will spend. It keeps you from spending money on things you don't require when protecting your workers. It's also easier to organize your safety plans when you work well enough.

Identifying Risks

The first part of safety planning involves reviewing possible hazards within the workplace. Every business has unique risks that must be curtailed to protect its employees.

Do you know of any safety concerns in your workplace? Are there actions or items in the area that might put people at risk? Knowing what is in your workplace and what concerns might occur is the first step to helping you prepare a safe work environment.

You can manage the risks within your business if you understand the threats in the area and how to manage them well. You have many measures to use when reviewing possible risks.

1. Think about what you're going to inspect first.

A safety inspection can help you identify risks in your workplace. But the analysis works best when you know what you're going to inspect and what you'll search for in your work.

Take note of anything in the workplace that might be potentially hazardous. Are there machines or devices that might be risky? Are there environments in the workplace that could be dangerous for any reason? Maybe there's a structure in your area that doesn't appear as stable or secure as you would wish.

Look around your workplace and see what you should look at before you start. It is easier to find potential security threats when you review spaces in your area that are out of the ordinary.

2. Consider possible issues that have come about as of late.

Many safety risks might be ones that have stuck around for a while, but sometimes the risks in your workplace are ones that came about recently. These include problems that might not have been an issue in the past but are becoming more prominent. Sometimes these issues might become more concerning when new processes are introduced. Look at how well these safety issues are coming, and use those details to figure out what you should inspect next.

3. Check what standards you have for managing different devices and routines.

What steps does your business follow surrounding how you manage different tasks and projects? Every operation in your business will have unique points and processes you must follow to be successful. Review these points to see how well your business is running and if you need to make changes.

4. Talk with managers and workers for details.

Sometimes an inspection won't cover everything about what's happening in your business. You'll need to talk with managers and workers for details on what they notice and what concerns they hold. It is easier to spot hazards when you get firsthand accounts from workers who have concerns over how a business is operating.

Speaking with other people about their safety needs can make the process of improving business safety easier for everyone. All workers will feel comfortable about what's happening in the workplace, as they feel their input is valued. You'll need to act upon whatever information the people provide, as offering solutions based on what fits will be critical to your success in making things work.

You can also consult those workers and managers after you complete your initial work task. You can ask them if they notice any positive changes in operations after you make some alterations.

5. Use a room-by-room analysis in your workplace about how well you can identify risks.

Every room or section in your business will have distinct operational needs. You can complete a room-by-room analysis of your entire work environment to see what fits and how your business is managing itself.

You can see if certain areas in your property have distinct concerns that require resolving. Sometimes a location might have unique needs you may not consider, while others might share the same problems.

6. Look at the initial ideas you might have for implementing safety measures.

You don't have to be fully committed to whatever changes you feel will work at this point, but you can use this time to identify potential safety measures that might fit your business. These include moves that will correct any problems you find while reviewing your worksite.

You can prepare a report on your findings and arrange preliminary recommendations for whatever might work. These findings can be as thorough as you wish, but make sure they work as recommendations without doing anything definitive yet. You will need time to figure out what is right and how you're going to plan your business well enough.

7. Create a plan for how you'll keep these measures running.

You can use your report to determine how well you will keep your work measures running well. These measures can cover anything surrounding your findings. The timeframe you use for maintaining these measures can vary, but you can spend as much time as needed to prepare a safer environment.

These initial steps are vital for helping you find possible safety threats. By starting slow, you can go toward reviewing more detailed concerns that might require support.

Best of all, this effort doesn't have to cost lots of money for you to manage. You can talk with your workers at various points to see what they need and how you can serve their demands for a safe workplace.

Sometimes the work involves finding you don't require certain things you're spending money on when trying to be safe. Your communications with your workers can help you dictate where you'll go from a safety standpoint while creating a safer approach to work.

Unique Safety Plans and Inspections For All Segments Of Your Business

After figuring out what you should check for your general business safety needs, you can start working on your workplace safety plan. Every workplace routine will be different, so checking on what each part requires and demands is ideal for success.

Your business will have multiple concerns that need to work when maintaining safety. Your safety planning effort should include help for managing every aspect of your business, including how you handle different safety concepts.

Your business will have multiple points to consider when getting your business protected and safe. These include segments such as:

- Electrical safety
- Fire prevention
- Hearing protection
- Bloodborne pathogen exposure
- Respiratory protection

You can review your current business operations based on how well you run all these aspects in your workplace and anything else that needs coverage. You'll need to start by looking at the needs your business has for safety purposes and how you can manage them as necessary.

You can keep your workplace safety costs down by focusing only on the solutions you require. To do this, you'll need to follow a few steps:

1. Gather any existing pieces of information you have on current workplace safety standards.

Review all your operating manuals for devices and equipment, plus check patterns of frequently occurring injuries, illnesses, or other concerns that arise in your workplace. Look for input from your workers and others to see what they have to say about your current safety efforts.

You can also see what trends are in your work industry and if you can manage those trends in some way. These unique points can change how you work, but they should also be relevant to your business while being simple.

2. Inspect your workplace to see opportunities for a safer environment.

Regular inspections of your business are critical for identifying problems. Check all operating procedures, review your equipment, inspect work areas, and contact your employees for details on what is happening in the environment and what needs help the most.

Your inspection can include a review of potential hazards, protective measures, work practices, and ergonomic issues. Keep note of anything you find, and ask other workers for help in seeing how anything you are reviewing can work.

3. Identify possible health hazards.

The health hazards in your workplace can include chemical hazards from materials you use or from poor ventilation, physical hazards that trigger excess noise, and biological hazards that can trigger occupational asthma or allergic reactions.

Your inspection can include checking on ergonomic risk factors that make it where people may physically struggle with some tasks after a while. You can also conduct quantitative exposure reviews to see how often people may encounter these issues.

4. Check on any prior incidents that happened in the workplace and see what caused these to occur.

Any injuries, illnesses, or near-misses in the workplace require thorough investigation. Review any incident reports filed to see what happened and why it happened. Look at what might have led to the failure and why no one bothered to fix the problem. The goal is to see if something could have been prevented while also seeing what can help stop such threats from happening again.

This aspect is vital for cases where you have experienced a certain event more than once. You can compare these instances and see if there are noticeable differences in these events or if there's a particular trend.

5. Determine the nature of whatever hazards you find, and see what controls may work for resolving these issues.

You should understand through an inspection what hazards can occur in your workplace. You can identify proper control measures to keep these problems from happening again. Temporary measures can work while looking for a permanent solution, but be sure you look at an answer soon to keep from spending more on temporary measures than necessary.

The goal of preparing safety plans for each part of your business is to reduce the risk of entering your work environment. Make sure you look at the unique things that need help and then plan your work based on whatever fits.

Review Your Wants vs. Needs

Every business has unique wants that they feel will make their workplaces more efficient and convenient. But sometimes these wants might be too expensive.

Sometimes you might think about what you want and plan to get it in the future, but that doesn't mean it will always work. Those assets you desperately want might not be suitable for your business, or they may be excessive.

This point is valid for workplace safety, as a business will require its needs more than its wants. The needs for safety are basic requirements a business has to fulfill to be successful.

A good way to compare the two is to consider how many needs and wants you may have. The number of needs you hold is limited, while you could have as many wants as you wish.

Your workplace safety needs will include things that have to be used to allow people to do their jobs. People will not be capable of handling their tasks if they're in unfavorable working environments where conditions may be hard. The work space may be too loud, or the ventilation may be poor enough to where fumes and other chemicals may stick around.

The best way to keep your workplace safety budget in check is to stick with your needs over your wants. You can add your wants later on as your business grows and you can afford to do this without risking anything else in your budget.

Check what equipment and measures are absolutely necessary for your business when planning your safety efforts. Install safeguards that prevent people from entering the wrong spots, for instance. Provide personal protective equipment or other items that can help people stay in work environments for longer periods without experiencing excess stress.

Educating your employees on how to use their equipment the right way also helps. They can learn how to handle materials well to reduce injuries while staying productive.

New safety technologies will eventually come about in the future. These items include automation features, mechanical controls and panels, and other items that help people complete their jobs without being too close to something. These features are convenient, but they may be too expensive for you at the moment. The costs for these materials may still drop as they become more commonplace and refined.

You can also monitor whether you'll require certain things in the future. The wants you have right now could become needs in the future, but there's no guarantee that will happen. Review your future needs and plan to add things when you need them, but don't try to get them ready too soon to where you might spend more money than what you require right now.

Sometimes those wants might be general preferences, but they may also be things that aren't suitable for your work plans. They might be materials that are too impractical or otherwise things that most people may not need.

Be certain when planning your workplace safety materials that you know what is suitable for work and you're not spending more on your work than necessary. Don't assume when your business grows and you have more money that the wants you had in the past will become needs, as you only need to think about things that are necessary right now. The needs are always the most vital point of the task.

Analyze Compliance Standards

Safe businesses always comply with the necessary standards. You can review how your business' safety standards compare with what the major organizations say about how to keep your business safe.

The organization you'll follow will vary by country. Each has different standards to follow, plus the cost to take a certification course with these groups will vary. Be sure to check the websites of these organizations to see what is open, and make sure to review any local standards based on your state, territory, province, or any other region where you do business.

OSHA Standards

The first group to consider is OSHA, the top workplace safety organization in the United States.

The Occupational Safety and Health Administration has essential standards for businesses to follow when keeping workplaces safe. OSHA states that all employees have the right to be in a safe workplace where they will not be at risk of harm. The goal of a business is to provide the necessary safety materials and guards to keep employees safe.

**Occupational Safety
and Health Administration**

OSHA has standards applicable to general businesses, construction companies, agricultural businesses, and maritime operators.

The goal is to eliminate potential hazards or keep hazards you cannot remove from being too severe. OSHA reports there are five things that can be done to protect your business.

This listing goes from what can be done first to the last and best possible thing you can do to protect your workers:

1. Provide Personal Protective Equipment or PPE
2. Use administrative controls to change the ways how people work

3. Use engineering controls to isolate people from whatever hazards are present
4. Substitute the hazard with something new if possible
5. Physically eliminate the risk as necessary

OSHA standards also cover various fields like these:

- How to handle hazardous materials
- Emergency action plans that address potential emergency scenarios and how to respond to them
- Respiratory protection
- Electrical wiring support
- How to use powered vehicles or machines, including forklifts, cherry pickers, and other battery-powered tools
- Hearing protection for all workers
- Guards for machines and other devices

OSHA has an extensive listing of standards for people to follow to provide a safe workplace environment. You can visit the OSHA website at osha.gov for details on what standards are available.

The website will help you see what you should do to become OSHA compliant. The measures you'll need to complete will vary surrounding your current business situation and how much effort is necessary for your business to reach compliance.

All of these details from the OSHA website are also free for people to use. Since OSHA is a part of the United States Department of Labor, the organization provides various free guides, posters, cards, and other materials for businesses to print and display on their work sites. These include documents in English and Spanish.

How Does an OSHA Inspection Work?

Planning your safety efforts is critical to preventing OSHA violations from arising in your workplace. OSHA will fine workplaces where safety violations appear. OSHA can impose these fines based on the severity of the violation, the probability of the violation causing harm, and the gravity of harm that could occur if something wrong happens.

These violations can appear during traditional OSHA inspections. OSHA's compliance safety and health officers can conduct workplace reviews to see how safe a site is. OSHA reviews can occur without advance notice in most situations, and any person who tells a company about an OSHA inspection in advance will be subject to fines and a possible jail term.

An OSHA inspection will involve a few steps:

1. An OSHA officer will provide one's credentials.
2. The officer then communicates with the worker representative to explain why OSHA is reviewing the site.
3. The officer will check all injury and illness reports.
4. A walkaround occurs where the officer and representative reviews work areas to find possible violations.
5. All found violations are documented and reported to managers as necessary.
6. The business will learn of the recommended changes for workplace safety.

7. The officer will send a report to OSHA with information on any violations that occurred, hazardous working conditions, how much time the company has to abate these problems, and any proposed penalties that may be necessary.

The inspection can take as long as it has to. The inspector needs to gather as much info on your business as possible to ensure you're staying safe and aren't violating any rules.

What Are the Most Common OSHA Violations?

An OSHA fine can be thousands of dollars on average, plus you could spend thousands of dollars more each day if you don't abate the issue before a certain date. **The highest fines from OSHA are worth $14,502 per violation. Businesses engaging in willful or repeated violations will be fined at least $10,360, plus that fine could go up to $145,027.**

Violations can become expensive if not handled or corrected soon enough. For example, in August 2022, a Chicago-area construction contractor had fines of nearly $400,000 over violations found in seven prior inspections. An additional $300,000 in fines was proposed after yet another inspection found fall hazards that weren't corrected.

OSHA applied these fines because the contractor was negligent in fixing these problems. Failing to fix them caused the business to become dangerous to workers and others nearby, and the fines will make it harder for the contractor to do business.

But what types of violations can lead to OSHA fines?

Some of the more common OSHA violations that businesses are fined for include:

- Improper fall protection
- Lack of respiratory protection
- Ladder stability and quality
- Lack of hazard communication
- Lack of eye and face protection
- No guards for machines
- Issues surrounding powered industrial trucks and other battery-powered items
- Scaffolding quality for construction sites

These OSHA violations can be reported by an employee or another party who notices these issues. Sometimes an OSHA representative can arrive at your site to inspect your space and see if you're committing any violations.

Your safety planning needs should focus on managing these concerns and preventing any likely problems that may develop. Planning your safety efforts based on common issues can reduce your risk of encountering OSHA violations and losing money on fines or efforts to fix anything that becomes too serious.

Necessary OSHA Forms

Sometimes an accident or injury may still occur at the workplace. You'll have to complete the necessary OSHA forms in cases where an injury happens.

But even then, you'll have to fill out these forms if no one is injured. The key is to provide a transparent look at how safe your business is while being direct on any problems that occur.

There are three OSHA forms you'll need to complete:

1. Form 300

Form 300 is a log of all work-related injuries and illnesses. The log includes details on the employee's name, job title, the date of the injury, where the event happened, and the illness or injury that occurred. Details on whether a person spent days away from work or remained at work but had a job transfer or restriction will also be included.

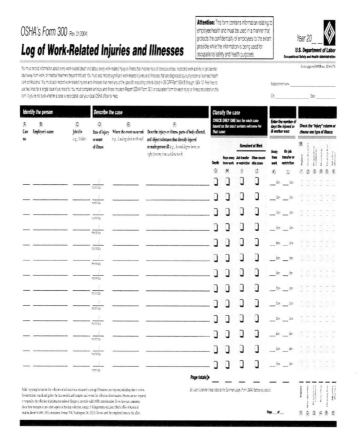

2. Form 300A

Form 300A is technically the second page of Form 300. Form 300A includes a summary of all work-related injuries and illnesses, including a summary of the number of cases involved, the number of days people missed, and the injury and illness types. The goal for a business is to have no injuries or illnesses on the document.

3. Form 301

Form 301 covers specific information on any injuries or illnesses on the job. It is an extension of the report you provide on Form 300. Form 301 includes specifics on the person who was injured or became ill. You can also discuss specifics on the case, like what the person was doing at the moment of harm, what object or substance harmed the employee, and details on whether the person was hospitalized as an in-patient.

All three of these OSHA forms are critical for your business, as you could be fined if you do not complete them or record data on them. Even if your business has no injuries, you should still specify that you did not have any on your forms. OSHA could fine you if you aren't compliant in getting this information out. The value of the charge will vary by each situation and will be higher if you are a repeat offender.

ISO Standards

The International Standard for Organization establishes various standards for operating different tasks. For workplace safety, ISO 45001:2018 is the standard you'll need to follow.

ISO 45001 was published in 2018 as a series of standards for reducing occupational injuries and threats. Any business that wants to prepare an occupational safety plan must follow ISO 45001 standards to be successful.

ISO 45001 is the current standard for businesses to follow. It replaced OSHA 18001:2007, a standard that was more reactive.

The details in ISO 45001 are too extensive to list here, as the official guide from ISO is about forty pages long. But some of the more prominent aspects of ISO 45001 to follow include:

- Understanding how to identify hazards
- Reviewing risks to safety and opportunities that may arise
- Gap analysis measures
- How to analyze the needs and expectations of all involved parties
- Operational planning and control
- Performance evaluation standards, including confirming how well people are adhering to new safety rules
- Improvement measures for prolonged safety like reviewing how well a business responds to different incidents and threats.

ISO 45001 works differently from other OSHA standards in many ways:

- There is a greater focus on understanding how to improve safety in the workplace while boosting performance standards.
- ISO 45001 standards also focus on a leaner approach to work. The effort includes using fewer parts in the work process to create a less complex and easier to manage system for work.
- Top management levels are more involved in the ISO 45001 process. Management teams should look at how well a project can work and customize a plan based on what fits business needs the most.
- Extensive employee training is likely required for the task. ISO 45001 encourages employee participation, allowing them to become more involved.

Whereas original OSHA standards were reactive and involved looking at what is in the workplace, ISO standards are about proactive measures. You're finding opportunities for improvement that are effective and will not force you into potentially hazardous situations that could cost your business more money than you can handle.

You can keep your business compliant while keeping costs down by reviewing ISO 45001 standards and seeing how your business compares with these points.

But how will you keep the costs down when using these points?

By using ISO 45001 standards, you will reduce the risk of workplace injuries. The work will help lower insurance costs, as the potential for your business to file a claim will drop. You won't spend as much money on insurance or worker's compensation costs when you keep your business safe based on ISO 45001 standards.

Implementation guides and handbooks are available for sale through various publishers. The cost for one of these books will vary but expect to spend about $100 for a copy in most situations. The cost is minimal in most situations and will give you the information necessary to keep your business safe and compliant without breaking your budget.

What About Certification Courses?

Your business can also go through an ISO 45001 certification course that can help you learn about how the standard works and how you can move forward with your tasks. But the cost of going through ISO 45001 certification courses may be too cost-prohibitive.

A smaller company could spend as much as $10,000 to undergo certification. But the charge involves more than studying to complete your ISO certification. Many of these costs entail:

- Courses to help you learn how the standards work
- An auditor visiting your site to review your compliance efforts
- Repeat auditor visits in cases where you have issues the first time around
- Filing legal documentation

You can keep the costs of receiving ISO 45001 certification down by focusing on guides and books that educate you on how the ISO 45001 standard works. Various guides are available to help you learn how it works, plus these can help you learn at your own pace without attending traditional classes that might cost extra to manage.

HSE Standards

The United Kingdom also has workplace safety standards for businesses to follow. The Health and Safety Executive or HSE is a UK government entity that supports workplace safety rules and the mitigation of occupational risks.

The standards for workplace safety HSE holds are in the Health and Safety at Work etc. Act 1974. The Act of Parliament lists the duties employers and employees have in maintaining a safe workplace environment.

The act lists multiple considerations for businesses to follow:

- An employer must provide a suitable workplace environment that is safe and does not produce potential health risks to employees.
- For cases where workers may be put into risky situations, an employer must provide the necessary protective measures and preventative standards for workers to follow.

- Any materials used in the workplace must be designed and built to be safe for use.
- Testing and examination standards must be clearly labeled for all devices and procedures. Such tests can help see how well these practices are working and if there are problems with existing standards.

Employees must also maintain their own health and safety while also protecting other people who might be impacted by their workplace actions and duties.

You can review the <u>Health and Safety at Work etc. Act 1974 online</u> to analyze standards for operation.

HSE Training Standards

All employers in the UK must provide safety training for work purposes. Employers must offer training to people at varying times:

- When someone is first employed
- When someone is first exposed to new risks
- When existing risks become more substantial
- If a manager notices an operator struggling in some form
- Refresher training is recommended every few years, especially when employees work on high-risk activities

These training rules are listed by the HSE and the UK government in the <u>Management of Health and Safety at Work Regulations 1999</u>.

Health and safety training courses are available throughout the UK, with online and in-person classes available. Most training courses will cost £525 **per person in most situations, although some advanced courses may cost £1175 or greater per person.** These courses are necessary for employers, managers, and engineers.

The information these parties can collect during these training courses can be delivered to employees in the workplace. All employers are expected to pay employees their regular pay rates during training sessions.

Safe Work Australia Standards

Australia also has unique standards for businesses in that country to follow. Safe Work Australia focuses on supporting workplace safety efforts throughout Australia.

Safe Work Australia concentrates on Work Health and Safety or WHS standards. Australian WHS laws established by Safe Work Australia require employers to provide safe work environments and training and support to employees.

The Work Health and Safety Act 2011 is the predominant act for workplace safety in Australia, but regulations are different in all states and territories around Australia. The Occupational Health and Safety Act 2004 is the main safety act in Victoria while the 1984 edition of that act is used in Western Australia, for example. The Australian Government Business website has information on specific standards to follow in varying states, including codes and regulations to follow and how workers' compensation is to be regulated.

Safe Work Australia offers training courses for employers and managers aiming to support all WHS standards. These courses cover various aspects for businesses to follow, including:

- How to maintain a safe workplace
- The proper handling and storage of various assets
- Training and instruction necessary for certain tasks
- Monitoring the health of workers
- Identifying the condition of different assets in the workplace

The cost for WHS courses will vary surrounding where you go. It costs about **$1,500 or more per person for courses,** with some places charging twice as much. Be sure when looking for WHS courses that you look around to see what courses are appropriate for whatever studies you want to complete.

CCOHS Standards and Training

Canada uses the <u>Canadian Centre for Occupational Health and Safety</u> as its main organization for supporting workplace safety standards. The CCOHS supports the production of standards for physical and chemical safety in workplaces around Canada.

Employers can encourage workers to take various CCOHS-based courses surrounding how to manage workplace safety standards. These courses are available through the CCOHS website and will vary in cost, with most programs being **$49 to $64 per person** to complete.

Workplace safety standards may also vary by province. All business operators in Canada must look at what standards they will need to manage.

HSA Standards and Training

Ireland uses the <u>Health and Safety Authority</u> as its organization for managing workplace safety standards. The HSA focuses on promoting proper safety standards in work while securing the inspection of all worksites.

HSA

An tÚdarás Sláinte agus Sábháilteachta
Health and Safety Authority

HSA has multiple training courses where people can study safety standards based on various industries. These include courses relating to farming, construction, healthcare, workplace transport devices, and schools.

Courses for study in Ireland include ones relating to risk assessment, safety management, handling chemical and biological agents, and physical and psychosocial hazards. Workers in the farming industry can also study how to safely handle slurry.

The cost to train people in Ireland will vary surrounding how many people require training. You can train people in a business with **fewer than ten people for €19.95 per course per person**, although the cost will drop when more people are involved in the learning effort.

2 Training

Your employees will require training to help them stay safe in the workplace. While no one wants to think about being trained or having to undergo extensive efforts to learn how to work, training is necessary for anyone who wants to go somewhere in a business. This point is especially vital for businesses where safe working practices are vital to manage.

Training helps your employees and others in the workplace understand what is necessary for work. There are various measures you can use when training people, with some options being available for free or at a low cost.

But whatever you choose, you'll need to look at how you're training your employees and how you're making your safety goals fit. Planning your training is essential to help you see what you want to do and how you're going to spend money on getting training programs ready.

So, how much does it cost for you to train an employee? The expenses associated with training employees are a critical part of what you'll need to get it right the first time. According to Whatfix, companies **spend about $1,200 per employee on training costs**.

Small businesses will spend more than $1,500 per employee, as they require more training to handle a wider assortment of duties. Small businesses also don't have as many people on hand to help, requiring more time for training.

The cost to train employees can also increase when you factor in technology, specific procedures, equipment, and anything else necessary. The lost time you'd spend having to train employees on safety standards can also be a problem, as you're taking time out of your schedule to handle various tasks.

Training your employees to be safe and understand your rules for work is vital to creating a protected environment where the risks are minimal. You can spend less on training when you get everyone on board while noting how your training plans will work.

Proper training is especially important, as you want your new employees to feel confident about what they're doing without questioning anything they would come across. Not training your workers well enough could be a problem, as they might not be willing to keep working if they're not certain what they should do. Training can also help encourage a person to want to work, so training someone well enough can make a positive influence on your business.

Reviewing Your Safety Goals

What do you want out of your business for safety purposes? Maybe you want to create a more comfortable environment for your workers, or you want your workers to stay protected near devices.

You can keep your training costs under control when you look at whatever safety goals you want to accomplish. You can do a few things to help you get to your goals:

1.   Consider the possible hazards in your workplace.

It is easier to prepare your training program when you focus on realistic hazards and issues in your environment. Complete a thorough review of your workplace to see what hazards you should discuss.

2.   Figure out who will run your training programs.

Management will operate training programs to educate workers. Managers should budget time and funds for training while delegating tasks to the proper groups. Communication is necessary between all parties, as the managers who will run these programs must understand what they're talking about.

Be sure whoever runs these programs also has the applicable training if necessary. Training standards to help managers learn how to educate workers will vary.

3.   Look at whatever systems you want to incorporate.

The training process also includes reviewing the systems you want to use when getting workers ready to handle different tasks. Training is about helping people understand unique safety systems or procedures that deserve note. Your managers can look at how well your information works.

4. Refresher training is also essential to plan.

Refresher training involves providing further guidance to people who have already undergone safety training. The training can occur once a year and cover topics relevant to the safety standards you want everyone to follow.

You can use whatever training plans you have, but be sure when planning something you know what's happening and that you have a smart plan for work. A well-defined training plan can improve how well your business runs while giving your employees the confidence they need to be successful and thorough.

Review Direct and Indirect Safety Costs

Your training should be based on whatever assets you have for keeping people safe. Training is more effective when you have the necessary materials on hand to teach people how to be safe in the workplace.

There are two types of safety costs to note: direct and indirect costs.

Direct Safety Costs

First, there are the direct costs associated with safety. Direct expenses are easy to calculate and can be attributed to protecting people and whatever losses you would encounter if someone were hurt while on the job.

Some of the direct safety costs involved in your workplace includes:

- Personal protective equipment
- Safeguards and other shielding materials
- HVAC systems and other features to keep air quality under control
- Lighting features to make a space easy for people to navigate
- Alarm systems and other things

There are also some direct costs relating to expenses that directly come from a workplace injury. These can relate to worker's compensation, legal fees, and medical expenses.

Indirect Safety Costs

The indirect safety costs for training involve unbudgeted and uninsured expenses that can arise when planning a training session. You cannot see how these costs change, but they are often more influential to your business than direct costs. The indirect costs could be worth several times the direct costs you're already spending.

The indirect safety costs for training include:

- Impact on productivity, including how well the training sessions help people understand how to stay safe
- Improved employee morale inspiring people to want to keep working
- Equipment protection
- Costs for recruiting or hiring new workers; existing workers will not be as likely to leave if they feel safe
- Not having to deal with OSHA fines or penalties

These indirect safety costs will keep your business functional, as training helps get everyone on the same page. The total value of indirect costs is impossible to figure in some situations, but the long-term impacts of these items can make a positive or negative impact depending on the situation.

Regardless of how much money you put into your training program, you will save money when you consider how you won't struggle with medical expenses, a lack of productivity, or a need to hire new people.

Preparing Safety Training Plans Based On Functionality

The next part of workplace safety training involves preparing your safety plans based on whatever activities people are more likely to manage.

You can establish your training plan with a few steps:

1. Analyze whatever training needs your employees have.

Look at your current safety record to determine what problems are present. Some of these issues may come from the work environment, while others could be from employees not performing well enough.

2. Conduct the necessary reviews to see what should work when you manage training.
3. Establish your training objectives.

Training objectives are what you want your employees to do after they undergo training sessions. You can create goals based on employee awareness, behavior, or procedures. Part of this also includes teaching employees how to build their skills when working.

4. Establish the necessary protocol for training.

The training protocol will cover the training methods you will use, whatever materials you have, and any resources you can access. Everything you provide should be essential to a person's job.

5. Get the plan up and running. Train enough people with your current plan.
6. Evaluate your plan to see how it works. You can revise anything in your work as necessary.

What Training Methods Are Available?

You can use various training methods in the workplace, with some measures being more budget-efficient than others. Some options can work for anyone, while others are only suitable for certain people.

1. Computer-Based Training

You can use computer-based training programs to help workers learn how to stay safe. PC-based programs, web-based programs, and interactive multimedia programs are useful items that can be shared among many workers. These may also be affordable, as they can work on computers already in your workplace.

<u>Whatfix lists</u> an assortment of training programs, with each featuring different programs and modules for people to complete. You can create a master account with a program and assign your employees specific modules for them to finish based on their workplace roles.

You shouldn't have to purchase new computers for computer-based training in most situations. Some of these programs could also be accessible on a worker's device, whether it is a mobile item or a desktop computer at one's home. You can plan computer-based training around whatever assets are available for work.

2.   On-the-Job Training

It is often easy to educate people on safety when you do it on the job floor. On-the-job training involves directly showing people how to manage safety standards. You can offer firsthand demonstrations of how to use certain devices or how to manage safety materials or guidelines.

On-the-job training motivates employees and helps them understand what is necessary for work. Some people may also have an easier time learning new things if they have firsthand experience with the subject matter.

3.   Coaching

Coaching is a one-on-one option for training that works for more specific needs. Every employee might have unique training needs, or they might have particular questions.

Coaching can help, but it is cost-effective if you have another employee coach the worker. People with more experience can coach the less-experienced workers.

Outside coaches can also be hired if you wish, but you could spend $50 or more per hour to hire one of these coaches. You'd have to review how each coach works and see if they can cover what you want to teach. Planning your own teaching efforts based on whatever standards fit your current business plans will be a better option.

4.   Planned Readings

Planned readings are for more technical training sessions that involve extreme specifics. For example, employees can review planned readings on certain devices they use in the workplace. These readings can include step-by-step instructions on things, plus photos showing what people can do may also appear.

Planned readings are effective if you make enough copies and have an in-person employee available to help prepare a reading. These readings can also be easy for customers to refer to, but make sure everything you prepare is easily accessible, and you have the necessary number of copies for everyone to manage.

Depending on the workplace and whoever you hire, you might need to get planned readings in different languages. English and Spanish-language documents should be available in most situations. Other languages may also be available, but it might cost more to acquire some of these documents.

What Training Methods Might Not Work Well?

Some training measures may not work well for your budget. For example, simulators may be too expensive and technical.

They also aren't necessary for most tasks, particularly routine ones that don't require many outside tools.

Simulators often work when teaching truck drivers how to operate vehicles. Air pilots can also use simulators to practice their flight skills. These simulators are extremely technical and require precision and accuracy. Most jobs don't require simulators, so don't bother with them if you don't have positions that might not be technical or specific enough.

Lectures may also be inefficient despite being potentially affordable. This training method works when you have a more massive business with dozens of employees. Lectures are useful when trying to talk with twenty or more people at a time.

A lecture is a classroom-style discussion where you talk with people about safety measures and what they should do. This option can be cost-effective, as you can get everyone in one place and talk about things with them. But be careful when planning lectures, as some workers might have more specific training needs.

Role-playing tasks may also not work, as simulated activities may not be as realistic as people might wish. Some people may also overcorrect themselves when trying to do something if they know they're being trained.

Outdoor training activities like rafting, rope climbing, sailing, or camp-related events can be fun, but they may not be effective either. While you can get your employees to build trust in one another, you're not teaching them how to do things in the workplace. It could also cost thousands of dollars to reserve a time at one of these outdoor training centers.

Look at how well your employees can learn things, and figure out something that works with care to help everyone with their studies. Everyone learns things differently, so look at what is open when finding an appealing plan for work that fits.

Additional Training Options

You can also consider many other training measures that are less expensive and easy to manage. Here are a few of the appealing training measures you can use that won't cost as much money as you might expect:

1. Social Media Learning

Social media platforms are appealing for helping people learn more about safety measures and standards. LinkedIn is the most prominent option available, as the professional-oriented social media platform has various online seminars and classes.

You can use LinkedIn Learning to help people learn about safety measures in the workplace and ways to maintain compliance standards. LinkedIn Learning has thousands of courses dedicated to various aspects of workplace safety. It costs $30 per person per month to use LinkedIn Learning, although team pricing options are also available.

2. Mobile Mentors

You can also assign certain workers in your business to be mobile mentors. These are people who will be available on-demand to respond to safety-related queries. These workers can respond by text message, email, phone, or anything else suitable.

Anyone you want to hire as a mobile mentor should be more experienced while also having shared values and experiences in the workplace. A regular manager can be a suitable mentor, although any employee who has been in the workplace long enough could qualify as one.

3.   Recorded Training

Recorded video training programs are also available for your convenience. Video training involves workers having access to video lessons by computer or mobile device. The videos you prepare can cover various aspects of health and safety protocols.

You can record your own videos and make them available on a private site for employees to access. You don't have to own your equipment to make these videos either, as you can rent something out for a bit to record your content.

4. Slack Meetings

Slack is a collaboration tool available for businesses to help people communicate with each other in real time. You can schedule an appointment with your workers on Slack to discuss workplace safety plans and get feedback from everyone.

You can lead a Q&A session with your employees, plus you can coordinate your work with other people through the platform, making it a more convenient solution for talking with others about your work and where you want to go.

The cost of using Slack will vary, with professional plans costing about $8 to $10 per user per month. Discounts are available for people who purchase annual plans.

You can also use a free Slack account if you prefer, but there are limits to what you can do here. Only two people can communicate with each other on the free version of Slack, for example.

How Can You Tell If Your Training Has Been Effective?

You'll need to keep your training effective to keep from spending too much money on getting people to handle their training tasks. An evaluation is essential to seeing if people are listening to your workplace safety training programs.

You can do a few things when training your employees to see how well they are learning new things:

1. Conduct an assessment test both before and after training.

Your assessment test can review if someone understands what was discussed during a training session. You can ask a person about one's safety skills beforehand and then talk about them after undergoing training. But make sure the assessment test is detailed enough and that you aren't repeating the same questions on the tests before and after training.

The training test can include a written or action-based platform. A written test can help you see if people understand various principles of safety. An action-based test will involve reviewing how well someone might work with certain tasks.

Be sure when looking at these tests that you're factoring in the participant's thoughts. Sometimes an employee might be more attentive or feeling more pressure when handling training activities, as that person knows they are being watched.

2. Ask questions during the training process.

You can ask your employees questions about what you are discussing while training. You'll receive real-time information on how well your employees are learning when you ask them questions about what you're referring.

Asking questions helps you see if someone understands what you're discussing. You can reinforce certain points you want your employee to review as necessary.

3. Complete a delayed evaluation.

A delayed evaluation is a review of how your employees are using their skills. You can see if the worker is handling certain tasks over what you discussed earlier.

You can plan your delayed evaluation a few weeks or months after the initial training. You can then take corrective measures for employees who might not follow the right rules.

4. Talk with your employees about what they're doing in the training process.

Sometimes you can get more details on how well training is working by talking directly with your employees. Ask them about how they feel about training, and see if they have any concerns they want to resolve or otherwise fix.

Your evaluation efforts can help you see if your training plans are working well. Proper training efforts are critical to helping to your employees, but make sure everything is planned right to where no one is confused over what can happen.

Avoid being too pushy around your employees when training them as well. You don't want to hassle your employees to where they feel they're being watched all the time. Allow your workers to handle things on their own, and let them feel that you respect their time.

3 Safety Consultants

One option for maintaining workplace safety involves hiring a safety consultant for help. You can hire a safety consultant to find opportunities to protect your workplace and its employees.

A safety consultant can be more affordable than you might expect. It can cost a few thousand dollars to hire someone like this, but it is more cost-efficient than other solutions when you consider the other points involved with training.

Your safety consultant's services can make a positive impact in helping you see what works. You may learn more about your safety needs than you realize when hiring a safety consultant for work.

What Does a Safety Consultant Do?

A safety consultant has three goals in mind when serving a business:

1. Ensure the business complies with all standards, including OSHA standards and any local rules.
2. Ensure all employees remain safe with the best materials, procedures, and safeguards.
3. Review possible risks and find ways to eliminate or reduce them.

The purpose of a safety consultant is to provide you with details on how to run your business with safety in mind. Your consultant will help you discover ways to keep your business secure without interfering with regular operations. The work is about protecting people to ensure those regular operations run without interruption.

How a Consultant Works

Here are some steps for how a safety consultant will serve your business:

1.   First, there is the inspection.

A safety consultant will start by assessing your needs and seeing what your business needs to stay safe. This point is the first thing a safety consultant will do when working for you. A consultant will start by reviewing your current safety-related practices and solutions. The consultant needs to understand what your business is doing before suggesting new ideas.

Employees will be monitored to see if they're handling things properly, and machines are checked to ensure they function well.

2. After the inspection, the consultant will list whatever problems are around.

The consultant will spend plenty of time reviewing everything around your workplace to spot potential problems. The consultant can check on things both while people are in the workplace and when they aren't there.

Sometimes a consultant can test the machines and other materials oneself, although that only happens if the consultant has actual experience with these items. You can ask your consultant about anything you have and if that person can review those items during the inspection process.

3. The consultant can check on any trends or causes surrounding the problems.

Every issue has a reason for it, and your consultant can help you see what is going on with your business. The analysis may take a while, especially if there are ongoing trends or recurring problems that keep showing. Sometimes these issues may be temporary, but in other cases, they might be an issue where you'll require some further help to make things work.

4. The consultant then prepares a response plan.

A response plan will include details on how the business will operate based on the consultant's recommendations. A consultant can write a manual or another response plan illustrating what the business can do. The consultant should have proper writing skills and understand how to manage risks to help create a suitable manual or report.

5. Consultants can also train employees as necessary.

You can request a consultant to help train your employees after coming up with the necessary solutions for work. The consultant can do this, but make sure the consultant understands all industry or local requirements for safety.

What If There Was an Accident?

A safety consultant can also be paged to a worksite if there is an accident or incident that results in harm. The consultant will arrive at the site and conduct an investigation into the issue. The review will include a check of the machines or processes involved and how they might have led to the event.

The consultant can also analyze the company's response to the incident and then perform a follow-up a few weeks or months later. The added inspection confirms that the business is actively fixing the issue.

But the consultant should only be one part of the accident analysis process. You can also ask other employees and observers for details on what caused the accident. Surveillance reports and other analytical points can also help you see what's happening and what problems might persist.

How Does Someone Become a Safety Consultant?

Safety consultants are trustworthy because they undergo extensive amounts of training and studying before they can become certified. Here are some steps for a potential consultant to follow:

1. The candidate must graduate from college.

First, a safety consultant must have a suitable college degree. A consultant can have a bachelor's degree in one of these fields:

- Occupational health and safety
- Biology
- Civil engineering
- Mechanical engineering
- Electrical engineering
- Another similar technical or scientific field

A consultant could also have a Master's degree in emergency management or another related field. A Master's in this field could have a concentration on occupational safety, emergency management, or corporate safety support.

1. The candidate then receives the necessary work experience.

The amount of work experience the candidate should have before becoming certified will vary by discipline. Some consultants become certified after one year, but others might wait as long as four years before taking a certification exam.

2. The person must then pass the necessary certification test.

The person should then undergo certification training to become a safety consultant. The Board of Certified Safety Professionals provides access to certification tests throughout the year.

3. The consultant will receive one's certification after passing.
4. Recertification points are required every five years.

Recertification is required from the BCSP to ensure consultants are up-to-date on safety standards.

What Certifications Are Available?

A safety consultant can hold one of many certifications with the Board of Certified Safety Professionals.

Here are a few of the most common certifications:

- **Certified Safety Professional** – A CSP must have at least four years of work experience with all safety measures that may work being preventative.
- **Associate Safety Professional** – An ASP will require one year of work experience. This option is suitable for people working toward their CSP certification.
- **Safety Trained Supervisor** – This person requires 30 hours of health and safety training and at least two years of supervisory work experience.
- **Construction Health and Safety Technician** – There are no minimum education requirements

here, but a candidate must have at least three years of experience in the construction safety field.

- **Graduate Safety Practitioner** – A GSP must have a bachelor's degree or higher in a Quality Assurance Program or QAP.

A Focus on EHS Management

A safety consultant can also help a business establish an EHS management system. EHS or Environmental Health and Safety is about improving workplace safety while reducing a company's impact on the environment.

An EHS management system allows a business to maintain productivity and sustainability while holding everyone accountable for their actions. It also helps people identify risks while creating a centralized approach to risk management that everyone in the business can follow. It becomes more accessible for everyone to manage hazards, plus workers can continue putting in efforts to improve.

Why Use a Consultant?

You could spend thousands of dollars a day to have a safety consultant on hand, but it will be a worthwhile endeavor. There are multiple good reasons why you should hire a safety consultant:

1. You can ensure compliance in your workplace.

A safety consultant will understand OSHA rules and standards, helping you stay safe while avoiding potential OSHA violations and fines.

2. A consultant will provide training to your employees.

A consultant can train workers to help them understand how to work in your environment. The consultant's teachings can help make processes more efficient.

3. A consultant will work independently from your internal affairs.

The problem with hiring someone in-house to manage your safety needs is that someone might be bogged down by various internal affairs in the workplace. An outside consultant will provide independent and neutral opinions and ideas for your business.

4. Consultants are always in the know about the latest standards in workplace safety.

Workplace safety is always changing, as new technologies and developments will influence what people can experience in safety. A consultant will let you know what fits in the workplace safety field based on the newest changes. You can use these points to see what can fit your work plans.

5. The consultant's expenses can be deducted from your taxes.

Hiring a consultant is a business expense, so you can use this as a deduction in your tax filing. The deduction means your taxable income drops, keeping your tax liability under control.

6. Your consultant can negotiate with the OSHA on your behalf.

Since your consultant understands OSHA standards, that person can negotiate with OSHA in cases where the consultant finds issues in your workplace. The consultant can discuss a plan with OSHA and set up a plan that helps you resolve issues while avoiding possible penalties or fines. Consultants often have experience dealing with OSHA, so hiring one who knows what OSHA is looking for always helps.

7. Your consultant can also prepare a new safety manual as necessary.

You can request your consultant to update or revamp any safety manuals you have based on whatever recommendations one provides. The changes will often make workplace processes more efficient and easier to follow.

8. You'll also manage your safety costs when you hire a consultant.

The consultant will help you review whatever safety expenses you have and find solutions to keep your business compliant while keeping overall costs down.

What Does a Consultant Cost?

The cost to hire a safety consultant will vary on who you hire and how much experience that person holds.

Expect to spend from **$1,000 to $1,500 per day** when hiring a safety consultant. The cost can drop to under

$1,000 per day if you hire someone for an extended period, but the terms will vary by service.

You could also hire a consultant to be on hand at your business for an entire year. It would cost $40,000 or more to have someone available throughout the year. This option works best for companies with at least fifty employees.

You can hire a safety consultant through one of four measures:

1. Hourly projects for short-term needs
2. Fixed bid projects that have a clear definition for work and a specific end date
3. Retainer model where you can request a consultant's services as necessary
4. Subscription model involving a consultant working a certain number of hours for you each month

Why Is a Consultant More Affordable?

While you'd spend thousands on hiring a safety consultant, it is still less than what you'd expect when having full-time resources for safety oversight.

Relying on full-time employees in your workplace to handle safety oversight may not be efficient enough. You could spend $50,000 or more per year paying for their salaries, and you'd be requiring those people spend more time than necessary on safety measures. A safety consultant ensures you'll allow your regular employees to focus more on the work they normally do.

Your consultant will also be more experienced in managing safety processes than your other employees.

Spending a few thousand on a consultant that can help for a bit is better than if you had full-time employees waste time handling these processes when they should be doing something else.

A personal employee may also struggle to stay in touch with the latest safety standards. Having someone who is always on top of the latest safety trends always helps.

How Do You Find a Safety Consultant?

You can find a safety consultant in your area by checking with EHS management teams. Environment, Health, and Safety management groups are organizations focusing on improving safety efforts in the workplace.

You can find various EHS management teams online through a simple search. But make sure when finding a talented consultant that you know what you are doing and you're finding someone who is trustworthy for the task.

4 Safety Marketing

Everyone in the workplace needs to be aware of the safety measures they have to follow. But the challenge of encouraging them to be safe and follow all measures can be daunting.

"Safety first" isn't a statement that creates a sense of ownership among employees. People may see that as a marketing slogan that doesn't mean much to them. You'll need to promote your safety measures to your employees to where they will feel motivated and ready to work with safety in mind.

Safety marketing involves more than monthly or quarterly meetings. It entails an ongoing effort to educate people on how they can safely work and manage various tasks without risking anything.

The goal of safety marketing is to have people feel they can working hard while staying safe. They should be confident in the work environment without worrying about the worst-case scenario. More importantly, the workers should feel that safety comes naturally and they don't have to overcorrect themselves.

You have many options to explore when promoting safety efforts in your workplace. Here are a few things you can do to encourage people to be safe and work their hardest.

Provide Clear Instructions

It is easier and more affordable to keep people safe when you're clear about what you want from your employees. Providing clear and sensible instructions to your workers about what they can do will help keep your employees ready for anything. They'll understand your work needs and be more efficient, keeping you from losing money from injuries and lost productivity.

Be sure the instructions you provide are sensible:

- Use step-by-step descriptions of whatever people can do on the job. Be detailed when letting people know what is necessary.
- Explain to people what they can do with different devices or materials in the workplace. Be clear about what you expect people to do with these items, and make sure they don't use them for unapproved actions.
- Provide instructions in whatever languages are necessary. This point is critical for workplaces that hire people who speak both English and Spanish.

Offer Enough Reminders

You can also provide multiple reminders around the workplace about the safety measures necessary for work. Explain to everyone what you want out of them and how they're going to complete their tasks for you.

A good idea is to create reminders that are positive and friendly while not being too overly aggressive. For example, saying something like "Caution: Loud area. Hearing protection is mandatory" might sound like something too patronizing to your employees. They might think you're talking down to them and that you're stating the obvious. Saying something in a sign like "Stay safe, wear hearing protection" can be helpful, as it provides a friendly safety reminder to your workers without sounding too rough or harsh. It explains that you respect your workers and want to help them stay protected while on the job.

Be careful when telling your employees what safety measures you want to handle. You don't want to make your employees feel unhappy with what they're hearing, but you still need to let them know what you want them to do from a safety standpoint.

Occasional Talks Can Also Help

You can talk with your employees on occasion to see what they are thinking about ongoing safety measures. This is a cost-effective way of helping because it lets you listen to your workers. You don't have to keep your workers away from their jobs for too long.

A typical talk can take about ten to fifteen minutes on average. You can ask a worker about what one is doing on the job, what one thinks about ongoing safety measures, and if there are any problems that need fixing.

The information you can get from your employees can help you see what to do. You could even learn about safety hazards or risks you never thought about when you ask your employees for help finding things in the workplace.

Encourage Breaks and Relaxation Measures

The workplace doesn't have to be all about work. You can also create a relaxed environment where people don't have to feel too much pressure.

Encourage breaks while on the job, including stretch breaks. Stretch breaks can last for about five to ten minutes and will give employees time to ease muscle tensions and keep their joints loose. The work reduces the risk of injuries from repetitive movements, plus it allows people to feel energetic and ready to keep working during the day.

For relaxation, you can create a quiet environment or room in your workplace where people can relax for a bit. A person can relax for about fifteen to twenty minutes, for instance. The worker can release one's tensions and start thinking positive thoughts, helping reduce stress and worry.

Breaks are necessary for helping people stay safe. People will feel motivated and confident in their work when they don't feel too much stress or pressure on the job.

Promote Updates

Do you have new workplace safety points you want your workers to know about? You'll have to provide details on these new standards to help people see what you want them to do.

Your safety marketing plans can include helping people see why your new safety measures are so valuable. You can educate them on how these processes work and what makes them beneficial. Providing regular information on all these new things can help you go forward in promoting a safe workplace culture.

One idea for safety marketing involves making your campaign about more than safety. You can discuss how a safe workplace is a more productive and efficient environment where everyone can feel trusted.

For example, workplace safety helps improve workplace efficiency. Worker absenteeism is reduced, plus there won't be as many shutdowns due to a lack of workers. It's also easier for people to feel confident about their jobs when they know they're safe.

A useful safety campaign will improve sales, hiring efforts, and employee morale. Sales will boost because your workplace will produce more materials or create a more favorable environment for customers. The reduced risk of hazards also ensures customers won't be hurt at your site, reducing legal costs and preventing negative PR from hurting your business.

You can also let your workers know about how safety can help bring in more new employees. Workers will feel better when employee turnover is minimal, as they will feel the environment is positive and everyone will be on the same page when working.

Safety is about more than helping people stay protected. It is also about creating a favorable environment where people will want to work. Make sure when marketing your safety plans you have an idea of how you're going to convey the benefits of safety to your employees.

5 Safety Software

What types of software programs are you using in your business today? You might not think about it, but you could be using several programs each day to complete essential tasks.

Today's businesses are spending more money on software than ever before. <u>All Business reports</u> that typical small or medium-sized businesses will spend at least $10,000 a year on technology, with some spending up to $50,000.

Many of these expenses involve application and platform integration, data protection, data management efforts, and email and ecommerce setups. The need to modernize old software or hardware is also an expense of note.

Businesses will use these software programs to boost productivity and sales. Some technologies are also necessary for improving workplace innovation. Other companies may use software to keep themselves from becoming obsolete.

Safety management software is one example of technology businesses can use today. Safety software can cover various safety-related functions in a business, allowing the company to stay productive.

You've also got a full assortment of programs available for use. The Capterra website provides details on all the programs available, including ones that offer free trial versions.

Safety software is critical to keeping your business afloat. But it can also be an expensive endeavor, as you could spend thousands of dollars on your software platform.

But you can keep from spending more than necessary when you make plans to find the right programs. Take note of a few things when looking for safety software that fits your work needs and budget while also being easy to manage.

What Does Safety Management Software Do?

Safety management software is also known as Environment, Health, and Safety or EHS software. This software option helps simplify processes relating to safety and protection in the workplace.

Safety management software monitors workplace behaviors and actions. It also identifies preventative measures and opportunities to improve workplace safety.

An EHS software setup can handle many tasks:

1.   Incident management

You can use your software to handle incident management reports. You can capture information on any incidents that occur in the workplace. The data can be reviewed for analytical purposes and to see what additional measures are necessary for protecting people in the workplace.

You can create a full report on an incident as necessary. The data can include details on what caused the problem, if there are any trends in the workplace that could have led to the issue, and how you could resolve the problem later.

2.   OSHA recordkeeping

Safety management software is also useful for helping you keep OSHA records. These include 300, 300A, and 301 reports.

3.   Automation

The automation features in safety management software can help you automate various administrative tasks. You can receive alerts or notes on anything unusual in the workplace based on whatever parameters you set. Your software can also help you trigger responsive actions to any problems that appear. A program can also create automated reports.

4.   Audit management

Your auditing plans will be easier to follow with safety management software. Your program can review hazards and risks while preparing unique analytical reports that show what safety measures you can incorporate to improve workplace efficiency.

5. Inventory and waste management

This aspect is necessary for businesses that handle chemicals, waste, and other potentially harmful materials. An inventory management system can help review how you're storing and using materials, plus you can keep everything organized through software to ensure nothing dangerous becomes lost or otherwise misplaced. You can use a program to track how many supplies you have while monitoring where they are located, for instance.

For waste management, a program will monitor the management and transport of waste materials. The analysis helps confirm your waste is being moved off to a centralized location, and helps you safely clear waste while ensuring everything leaves safely and without risk.

6. Specific functions

Some programs may also provide help for very specific functions. For example, Aries is a program that helps you review and test fire safety systems.

You can use as many safety software programs as you wish. But the programs should be suitable for operation while also being easy to follow. Anything that can integrate with one another is also a plus, as these programs will be easier for people to support in most situations.

Why Use Safety Software?

You might not think that safety software is essential, as you would figure you could handle these tasks yourself. So why is safety software important for your business?

Safety software will ensure your business remains compliant with OSHA standards. It also automates the data collection process, helping you run your business well without risking problems.

Your business will also become more sustainable, as you can spot risks and find corrective measures that can work before anything wrong happens.

You can also improve employee morale through safety software. Employees will feel confident when they know their business environment is safe and under constant analysis and review.

What Does Safety Software Cost?

As convenient as safety software can be for your business, it could also be expensive in some cases. You could spend **at least $2,000 per year** on safety software.

Most safety software providers will charge $200 or more per month for access to their programs. These companies may also charge this value every year.

Companies that want to acquire full-scale software platforms will spend even more money on the work. A complete system can cost $50,000 or more to use, but an average business will budget about $300,000 on its programs. The budget is good for the initial investment, regular maintenance, and any changes the business requires.

Expect to spend more on a custom program than an off-the-shelf platform. Whereas a customized system will cost tens of thousands of dollars, an off-the-shelf platform that is mostly complete will require a one-time onboarding fee and an annual or monthly fee to access the system.

What Factors Go Into the Overall Cost?

You can prepare your safety software well when you review the factors that go into what you'll spend on something. Here are a few factors that will influence what you might spend:

1. Implementation

The implementation process involves integrating your software into a workflow. You're trying to get your system working in the necessary platform in this measure. The effort of trying to get the program to work in your system will influence the cost.

2. Configuration

The configuration process can include adjusting your software to meet special procedures. But sometimes, it costs extra to configure your software because you're trying to customize and adapt it for different needs. A program might work differently on one platform versus another, for example. You could spend more on software if you have to configure more things.

The integration process can also go into the configuration effort. Integration involves allowing multiple safety programs to communicate with each other. These programs can share their information with you and keep your information accurate and consistent.

3.   Customization

You'll spend more on software if you customize it to include extra features beyond what the original layout includes. It is less expensive to configure your software than to customize it and create new things from the ground up.

4.   Maintenance

Maintenance charges involve keeping your software running and protected. Regular updates and monitoring may be necessary, especially if you're storing sensitive material.

5.   The number of users

The number of people who will access your program can influence the price. While the cost per user might drop when you have more people on hand, the expenses can still add up.

6.   How many sites your software will be available on

Your software program can be accessible in many locations. You can order a single-site program that is accessible in one spot, but it will cost extra for you to use a program in more areas. Licenses are necessary for allowing multiple users or devices to use something.

7. Support

Consistent support is necessary for keeping your software afloat. A software provider will charge extra for access to the customer support team in many situations. You'll require access to help fix bugs and other issues in your program. Troubleshooting may also be necessary for some situations, as software programs are always evolving and may have problems that weren't found the first time around.

The extra support charge is necessary for keeping the support team intact and ready to help people who need assistance. Since the support team for some software programs might be available twenty-four hours a day, there's a need to pay for everything well enough.

How Many Users?

One way you can save money on software is by looking at how many users will use your program at the start. You won't be able to buy a straightforward software program and install it on most devices in most situations. You'll have to get licenses that allow you to access the content.

Software developers require you to purchase access to their programs through licenses that allow a specific number of people to reach the content for a limited time, usually for a month or year.

Software developers demand people pay for licenses because they want to retain their copyrights. You will pay for the right to use the program based on whatever rules the owner establishes. The terms are based on the EULA or End User Licensing Agreement the developer produces.

The EULA says you have the right to use the software because the developer is giving you permission. You are agreeing in the EULA that you cannot copy or sell the software to anyone else. You also cannot edit or adjust the fundamental aspects of the program, although what constitutes as "fundamental" will vary by the developer. The EULA also protects users from legal liabilities that the software copyright owner might enter.

The agreement keeps you from using a program on too many devices. You will be limited to using the software on one computer or device. There might also be limits over how many user accounts can access the software.

Make sure you look at how many people are going to use your program at the start. Look at how many locations or devices you'll need the program on, plus review how many people will require accounts. You will be charged based on the number of locations or accounts involved, so check the terms before spending money on something.

For example, you might have a program that costs $45 per user per month. If you have ten users, it will cost $450 per month to use the software.

Some companies may offer volume discounts as well. The company that normally charges $45 per user could also charge $35 per month if you have more than fifty users or locations. Therefore, a business with sixty users would spend $2,100 per month to access the safety software.

Look For Free Trials

Some safety software providers offer free trials of their programs. A trial lets you test a software program and see how well it works.

This feature helps you see if a software program is useful before committing to a purchase. You can keep from wasting money on programs that might not work well for you if you test something first.

But there are a few things to spot when finding a free trial:

- Some companies may limit what you can do with a program during the free trial period. They will ask you to purchase the program to get full access to everything.
- The length of a free trial will vary, but it can go for about seven to fourteen days in most situations. You'll need to spend enough time with your program to see if it works and is suitable for your plans.

- You may have to provide credit card or payment information to the provider before you start your free trial. You'll need to submit a form or request to cancel your subscription to the program before the free trial ends to avoid being charged anything.
- Not all software providers will offer free trials.

Since there's a limit to how long your trial will last, you'll need to use your program often within that timeframe. Do not delay when using your software, as you'll need to check on how well it works before the timeframe expires. The features in your program could be vast, so using it soon enough is vital to see if your program will work as necessary.

Look For Self-Configuration Software

One idea for safety software you can use entails finding a self-configuration program. Configuration entails you being capable of adjusting the software as necessary. You can edit the program yourself if you prefer.

Look for a program that lets you configure its features yourself. The reasons for using self-configuration software are plentiful:

- Self-configuration is significantly cheaper than customization. Because you're not hiring someone else to customize your program, it is easier to run something.
- Your self-configured program will help you complete tasks faster. You'll require fewer steps to manage different tasks.

- You will have more control over your program and how it works when you configure it yourself.
- You can adjust the program to include more functions and developments as necessary.
- It is easier to maintain self-configured software. The underlying system will stay the same even if various forms and other features appear different. Vendors can update and fix your program without having to fumble through specific changes it doesn't recognize.

Remember that self-configured software is about keeping your program functional and useful. It should provide a better approach to work that is easy to follow without being complex.

What About Free Versions?

Some safety software programs include free versions where you don't have to pay anything to use the system. This point sounds exciting, but these programs aren't going to work well. A free edition is not going to give you everything you want out of a program. It is only intended to preview what you can expect out of the full version, which will likely be more viable for your use than the free one.

A free edition of a program will include an extremely limited number of features. For example, a free edition may not include any configurable features, plus it may not include full communication or reporting features. Free versions may also not offer mobile support.

A software provider should offer details on what a free version of a program includes before you agree to use it. You may find that paying for the entire program may be more effective than sticking with a free edition. Look for a free trial for the official product instead of a free downloadable edition to get a clearer idea of what to expect from the system.

What About Open Source Programs?

Open source software is an exciting option for businesses looking to save money on various operations. Open source software is a program available through a license where the copyright holder allows people the right to use, change, and distribute the software and its source code to anyone who wants to use it. Those people can use that software for any reason.

An open source program will be less expensive on average than a typical commercial program. Community members will develop and maintain the program, as they all have access to the source code. It costs less to download and access the program than to purchase something else that was prepared through a professional group.

Your open source program will also be easy to adjust. You can customize and edit it based on whatever needs you have for the program later on.

An open source software program sounds appealing, but that doesn't mean it will be useful. You'll still have the pay for the program, although that cost will be less than what you'd spend on average. But the problems with open source software are plentiful:

- Security vulnerabilities can become a problem with some open source programs. These problems can become worse if they come from improper programming on your end.

- Open source programs don't come with warranties for use. Since volunteers are responsible for developing and managing these programs, you won't get access to any warranties.

- Any developers who test the software will not be liable for faulty issues in your program. While they will see how well these programs work, the results they get from their testing plans may not be the same as what you experience.

- Some developers could unintentionally violate copyrights held by other companies. These developers might copy from other parties without recognizing the copyrights, leading to possible violations.

- Support solutions for open source software will not be as effective, as your edition of the program may be unique to your business. Anyone who wants to help would require an exact copy of your program and review the code from there to find something wrong. You'd also have to explain to someone what you're trying to get from a program and how you're going to make it function.

Remember when looking at open source programs that they aren't always going to work as well as you wish. These can be hard to prepare and use, plus you won't always get the best results from them.

What's more is you'd require plenty of coding and programming knowledge to figure out how to get an open source program ready. The program might be too complicated, and you might not have anyone in your workplace capable of managing the program.

You could hire a software developer to help you program your open source software, but it could cost anywhere from **$50 to $100 an hour to hire someone to help**. The cost would offset any potential savings you'd get from using an open source program.

Hidden Costs of Open Source Software

You'll find many hidden costs in your open source software program. While there are no license fees, you will have to spend extra on things like:

- New hardware you might require for some programs
- Support and maintenance costs
- Costs involving unique features or functions
- Third-party app support; this point is for cases where your open source program can integrate with third-party programs you might have to acquire separately

- Warranty costs; you might have to acquire a separate warranty from another provider
- Liability costs, including direct and indirect liabilities

Check how your open source software will work and review what you might spend to make it more functional. While you won't pay extra to get the initial program, the expenses for using it will be noticeable. Make sure the expenses involved aren't too costly to where a traditional program might be more affordable for use.

What Do You Require Now?

An open source software program with more modules and features will cost more for you to use than something else. More detailed programs will require more effort and programming, thus costing extra.

Take note of what you need safety software for before purchasing something. Make sure the features in your program cover everything you need and that there isn't anything that seems unnecessary or excessive in the program.

Check the devices you have as well to see if what you have today can run the software you use. You can always replace the computers you have later, but you might have to get new software to keep things running.

Do You Actually Need Safety Software?

While safety software can help you maintain your business, you might be curious about whether it is really necessary for your entity. You can tell you will require safety software if you agree with any of these concerns:

- Your workers are struggling to find EHS data.
- You aren't maintaining your business well, or you're not keeping track of everything you use.
- You don't have enough time to manage some of the safety functions in your workplace yourself.
- It is challenging for workers to compile reports, let alone read them.

Safety software can make a difference when trying to keep your workplace secure. But make sure when finding a program you have one that fits your needs and isn't too complex or otherwise hard to follow. A successful program will be helpful in keeping your business safe, but make sure you don't spend more money than necessary on something you won't require.

What About the Computers Themselves?

The last aspect to see about safety software involves the computers that will run these programs. It is generally best to replace these computers every three to five years. Regular replacements help your business stay intact and up-to-date on the latest tech functions.

Starter Story writes that an average business will spend anywhere from **$500 to $5,000 a year** on desktop computers, laptops, monitors, mobile devices, and other things necessary for operation.

You could always use refurbished used computers that cost less, but their capabilities may not be as strong as what newer models feature. There's also the option to add upgrades to existing computers, but computers can only handle so many changes and updates until they have to be replaced altogether.

Be sure when looking at your safety software you have suitable computers that can handle these programs. Look at how many computers you have, and incorporate the number of computers you have into your budget when figuring out what you'll spend on the software you will use.

6 Safety Researching

Businesses often don't think about safety research that much. They often assume safety standards in the workplace are consistent, and you don't have to think too hard about what to do. But safety research can be essential in helping you improve upon your existing tools and measures for managing safe operations in the workplace.

The goal of safety research is to enhance existing workplace safety rules and standards. There is always room for improvement when encouraging workplace safety, and your research plans can help you find a way to protect everyone.

Research is about finding new ways to do things while seeing how to improve new things of value. Your research plans can make a positive impact on how you run your business and make your safety efforts more viable. More importantly, research can help make your safety measures more affordable and effective while not requiring you to use as many assets.

How Does Safety Research Work?

Safety research is a practice involving reviewing how safety works in the work environment and what can help protect workers. Safety research follows a few steps:

1. First, accident data is gathered based on company reports.

Accident data can be collected based on OSHA Form 300, 300A, and 301 files or anything else you might utilize based on local standards. Accidents are analyzed based on how they happened, where they occurred, and other noticeable trends.

2. The trends are reviewed based on what is in the workplace.

The trends can be analyzed based on what machines or procedures are being used or what the working conditions are like. Anything that influences harmful workplace conditions can be interpreted as trends if they happen enough times.

3. You can make recommendations to keep these injuries from happening.

The analysis can help identify possible recommendations that can stop injuries. The recommendations should be based on what can help reverse trends. Safeguards that can protect people from certain problems can also work, but the goal is to find ideas to keep such trends from being persistent.

4. The recommendations are implemented, and the effectiveness of these measures will be analyzed to see what problems persist and if old issues were resolved.

The safety research process could take weeks or months to handle, as it needs time to see how well different practices are being managed and if there are noticeable problems involved.

The overall effort helps determine what can protect your workers and create a safer environment for everyone.

But the process can also be expensive if you don't think about how well it can work.

Who Completes the Research?

A professional or freelance safety researcher will complete the research. The safety professional will be certified to handle safety-related tasks and should have a certification with the BCSP to handle tasks.

The researcher will collect and organize data based on what one observes and notices in your work environment. The research then analyzes the data to not only solve problems but also review potential trends that may occur. The work involves checking on short and long-term potentials for workplace safety.

The researcher typically works on one's own, although an assistant may be brought in if necessary. The researcher should provide info on this point beforehand, especially since the assistant may require you to spend more money on the work.

What Does It Cost To Handle Safety Research?

Research costs can be high at any business, and this point is valid for safety research. The research process requires you to do many things:

- You have to hire outside professionals to help you review safety practices. These include people who are certified to work as safety experts.

- The analysis can take weeks or months to complete, especially if you are noticing any long-term trends that are hurting your business.
- The scope of your research can be as narrow or vast as possible. It could involve multiple tasks that require analysis, especially if they link together.

Researchers can work at varying rates, with many researchers going for at least **$50 an hour**. The total can add up if you keep that researcher on hand for too long.

You could also hire a freelance researcher who is not affiliated with any organization. This option is cheaper, as you could spend **$20 to $30 an hour** on someone's services. But the freelance researcher might not have experience in your field, or that person might do things differently from someone else who is a little more professional.

What Fields Do You Need To Research Right Now?

Deciding how you're going to plan your research can be a challenge. You can focus on studying what you need at the moment and what assets you have right now. Review your current fields and figure out any opportunities yourself to see what fits. You can use this plan to figure out what fields require research right now while keeping yourself from studying areas that might not be necessary.

You can hire your researcher to assist you as necessary. You don't have to keep that person on your payroll, plus you might not have to pay for one's services on a retainer. But you'll have to pay attention to your research needs and plan a service that works well with your budget while following whatever might interest you the most.

What About New Developments?

There are always new developments in the safety industry that you can utilize when finding new ways to protect people in the workplace. You can review whatever developments are happening and find ways to prepare your business to meet these needs.

What Types of Developments Can You Study Today?

You've got an array of developments to explore when looking at workplace safety. The trends in the workplace safety industry are always going to keep growing and diversifying, so understanding what is available in today's field will be essential to your success.

Here are a few of the more prominent workplace safety developments you can study:

- Smart PPE equipment can gather data on the user's health while it is being worn. The PPE can review a person's blood pressure, heart rate, and other factors, helping identify possible changes that might occur when someone enters specific situations.
- Holistic approaches to workplace safety could fit a business. The work includes focusing on the physical, emotional, and mental safety of the employees.
- Predictive analytics is moving into many industries, and the safety field is one of them. Businesses can

predict when certain risks can occur based on workplace actions and determine what changes can be made to prevent problems from happening.

- You can also research points on how blockchain functions can help you record your safety information and make it more accessible. Blockchain research can be more complex, but it can provide details on how you can share your info with others and build upon what you currently use.

Your studies can help you see how these concepts can work in your environment while planning a unique approach to safety research that fits your needs.

The essential part of safety research is there are no limits to what you can discover during the research process. Safety research works well when you understand how the practice works and find a reasonable plan for the task.

Be sure you have a suitable safety research plan in mind when getting this aspect of running your business ready. The research you prepare will be more effective when you have a better idea of where you're going with the work.

7

Tendering and Procurement

Tendering and procurement are essential aspects of business safety, as they involve acquiring the goods necessary for keeping your business safe.

Tendering involves the process where an organization will prepare plans for figuring out which vendors will supply them with safety materials. Your business will go to the external market to find organizations that offer the necessary items for your safety management needs, whether it entails PPE, machine guards, or whatever else is necessary for protecting your workers.

Procurement involves the acquisition of said goods and services. You'll select a vendor from the tendering process and then negotiate a contract with said group.

This practice sounds like traditional shopping, but it is more than searching for something viable. Tendering and procurement is also about seeing what the best deals are while finding suitable providers who can manage your needs. It involves preparing long-term relationships with vendors who can help you with your assets.

Tendering and procurement can make a difference when helping your business stay safe. But the practice can be expensive if you aren't careful enough.

Many vendors might charge more money for your safety materials than necessary. They might take advantage of your needs, as you might be willing to pay extra to keep your workers secure.

Understanding how the procurement and tendering process works is vital to keeping your business steady without risking possible losses or other threats. You can use multiple points to help your business stay secure and functional.

Planning a Tender and What It Can Include

The process of procuring items for workplace safety should start with an analysis of how you're going to prepare a tender. A business tender can entail requesting a traditional quote for workplace safety materials or services. But it could also involve a formal contract that spreads out your expenses over time.

By accepting bids or tenders, you are telling other workplace safety service and material providers you're serious about obtaining materials from these organizations. You are willing to spend money on your assets, and you've got details in your tender listing what you want to get out of the work.

A tender should include:

- Details on what assets you want, including quantities
- Any incentives you might offer to a provider
- How someone wants to provide a schedule of prices
- Options the providers can propose for submitting your content
- The terms of acceptance
- How long an offer is going to be good for
- Details on whether the bid will be for a lump sum of money or based on unit prices
- Any additional specifications you may request; you can be as thorough as necessary

The bidders can analyze these points and come up with suitable bids for services. They'll let you know how much they will spend managing your workplace safety needs. You can then use these bids to compare what is available and figure out which one you're going to procure.

FORM OF TENDER

[address]
[contact numbers]
[Date]

Mr [name]
[Job Title]
The Company Limited
[address]

Dear Mr [name]

[Tender reference number and Title]

We would like to offer to supply the above Goods or Services at the firm and fixed prices shown in the enclosed pricing schedule.

Our tender remains open for acceptance for a period of ninety calendar days following the tender closing date. It is confirmed that the [   ] Terms and Conditions are acceptable.

This Tender fully complies with your Specification.

[Attention is drawn to some innovative proposals at the back of this submission].

Should you need anything further, it can be supplied by the undersigned at the above address.

Yours sincerely

The number of tenders you'll get will vary based on whoever expresses the most interest. You could get a couple of tenders, or you could find dozens from various groups. You can choose the specific number you want, but be sure you've got a diverse array of tenders that fit whatever unique needs you have.

The tenders you receive will typically be in letter form, so read all the words carefully to see what you'll get from your content. Some may also provide more comprehensive presentations that offer details on everything involved and how it can be to your benefit. Always pick what you feel is right for your business, and don't assume that the flashiest or most interesting thing in the lot will be viable enough for your use.

What Should You Do When Reviewing Tenders?

The tender review process can help you determine which bids are the best ones for your needs. You can analyze tenders to see if they offer the materials you need at prices that are suitable for your business.

You might assume the lowest bid will be the most appealing, as it won't cost as much money for you to hire someone for your needs. But just because one offer is lower in value doesn't mean it is more valuable or useful for your business.

Review a few points when finding a tender for your safety needs:

1. Look for details on the bidder's history.

Many bidders will have websites where you can learn more about what these groups offer and how they can serve your needs. You can check a website to see how well a bidder works and what you can expect from that entity.

2. Look at the evidence a bidder provides surrounding one's assets.

Make sure whoever you contact has the assets necessary for you and that they are of the best possible quality. Again, you can see what details the bidder has on one's website.

3. See if the content the bidder provides is relevant to your needs.

What types of PPE do you require? How many things will you need to replace as time passes by? Are the prices suitable for your current budget, or are they better for later when your cash flow might improve? Look at the details the bidder provides and see if you've got enough information for whatever might work at a time.

4. Make sure the materials comply with whatever specifications you have.

The materials the bidder provides should fit with the unique specifications or demands you have for work. Look at how well the materials fit your needs and that you've got a suitable plan for work that helps.

You can always contact the bidder if you have further questions about the tender. The bidder should be ready to promptly respond to you and answer whatever questions you hold.

MEAT Criteria

One idea for selecting a tender that fits your business is to use the MEAT criteria. The MEAT criteria help you identify the Most Economically Advantageous Tender.

Instead of focusing on whoever has the best price for services, you'll look at whoever might be the most viable for your safety procurement needs.

MEAT is a concept used by the <u>European Union Procurement Directives</u> that can work for any business worldwide.

The MEAT criteria you can follow involve:

- The quality of the assets
- The price or cost based on cost-effectiveness or the net cost divided by positive changes in the workplace
- The technical merit of the provider
- Whether the safety materials are functional or effective enough
- How accessible the safety items are
- Whether these items are innovative or functional
- Environmental benefits, including whether these will keep your business from spending more on energy costs
- Service needs, including how much you'd spend on servicing your assets
- Assistance available from the vendor
- Delivery terms, including when you'll get your items and how you'll receive them

You can incorporate these criteria in your tender form, as you can request your bidders to provide details on all these points. You can place these in any level of importance you wish.

The criteria should meet a few conditions:

- All criteria should link to the subject matter surrounding the contract. It should be specific enough to where you can make a fair assessment over whatever might fit.
- The criteria should meet all local specifications and rules, meaning you'll receive the assets you require based on local law.
- There should also be a way to communicate with someone in case you have any questions or concerns over whatever you're trying to offer to someone.

The price of each tender will still be vital to your analysis, but the MEAT criteria can go into the work to determine which is more effective. Something that has more favorable points might be more viable to your business even if it costs a slightly higher amount of money.

Whatever the case, anything that could be considered abnormally low will not fit. Anything too cheap might be poor in quality, or the provider might not fully understand what is being made available. Compare the criteria you review versus their prices to see if there's a noticeable change in quality between offers.

What Happens In the Procurement Process?

Procurement is the next part of your safety supply chain. The procurement effort occurs when you find someone who can provide the necessary safety materials your business requires.

These are multiple forms of procurement you can manage:

- **Direct** – You'll acquire the safety materials you need through a direct procurement process.
- **Indirect** – This process involves receiving goods and services that aren't related to safety. But these assets may still be vital, like marketing services to promote workplace safety.
- **Goods** – The good procurement process involves gathering physical items you can hold as inventory for your safety plans.
- **Services** – Services involve human-based practices where people will provide safety-related services. Maintenance workers or repair providers can count as services.

How Does the Procurement Process Work?

The procurement process involves a few steps after finishing the tendering effort:

1. After choosing your tender of interest, you'll negotiate the price and terms for your tender.

Make sure you have multiple options for acquiring your assets. Set up the terms that are the most necessary for your business and request they are met before sticking with anything.

2. Prepare your purchase order.

Your purchase order includes details on what you're acquiring and how much you're spending.

3.   Receive and review your goods.

Check your shipment and compare it with what was on your purchase order. Did you get the items you requested? Are there any damages to your items? Make sure everything meets your expectations before going forward.

4.   Three-way matching can work at the next point.

Three-way matching involves comparing your purchase order, the order receipt, and the invoice. Everything should match together. You can highlight all the things that were incorrect between these documents and share these details with your vendor to show you're not going to pay for certain things you never got. You'll avoid paying for what you did not receive or authorize when you use three-way matching.

5.   You can approve your invoice after the three-way match is accurate. You'll arrange your payment at this point.

You can approve and pay your invoice when everything is complete and thorough. Review your business' accounts payable process and how it can get payments out based on invoices. The practice should be standardized to account for everything that might happen when taking in a payment.

6.   Keep records of all payments.

Proper bookkeeping is critical for confirming payments and tracking possible issues. Your records can confirm what you're spending and help you when you're reordering your assets. Accurate payment info can also help you with the auditing process while also calculating taxes the right way. You can also resolve possible financial disputes within the business if you have clear records.

7. You can reorder items as necessary if you keep the same data.

The reordering process is easy when you have all the data needed to complete the task. Make sure the reordering data is consistent, and you have info on what you're trying to acquire.

Strategic Partnerships

The process of obtaining safety materials through the tender and procurement routine is sensible, but the lowest bid for services might still be too high. So what can you do in cases where this becomes a problem?

You can establish a strategic partnership with a service provider to help you reach better purchasing deals. A strategic partnership involves two or more parties sharing resources to help each other succeed. The link comes from non-competing groups who want to help each other.

A strategic partnership can help your business keep from spending more on workplace safety materials. But it will also involve some extra work on your end to improve the connection between your partner business and yourself.

The most obvious part of your strategic partnership involves communicating with someone who can help you with your needs. The partnership should be complete enough to where everyone in the agreement can support the terms, but it should not be something that undermines any side.

Types of Strategic Partnerships

You can enter one of various strategic partnerships when finding someone who can provide workplace safety materials:

1. Marketing

A marketing partnership involves referring people to another business where you are acquiring your safety materials. You can promote the vendor's wares and list signs showing you use their products and services. You could also incorporate the vendor's work into your social media posts or other messages you send to others.

2. Supply

A supply partnership will involve an exclusive contract where you're exclusively using a vendor's products. You can use this point to promote your loyalty to a group, improving your potential to pay less for services and materials later.

3.   Supply Chain

A supply chain partnership is different from a traditional supply partnership. In a supply chain partnership, multiple groups will work together to prepare a safety plan. You can incorporate as many vendors into the supply chain partnership as you wish, especially if you find ones that won't charge more money than others. Some of these partnerships can be exclusive ones that provide proprietary parts made exclusively for your group.

4.   Referral

A referral partnership is where customers at one business will refer other people to the other business in the agreement. This effort sounds appealing for cases where the two sides are related in some way, but there's no guarantee every customer will want to support a certain plan. Customers may require incentives to encourage them to refer people to something.

Can a Partnership Be Competitive?

Some strategic partnerships might be a little more competitive than others. These partnerships can appear in one of four forms based on the amount of interactions between the businesses and the conflict involved:

1. Procompetitive Alliance

A procompetitive alliance entails there being little conflict between the sides, but there's also minimal interaction. This connection entails vertical integration, a practice where multiple stages of operation between different companies connect together.

2. Noncompetitive Alliance

The conflict remains low in a noncompetitive alliance, but the two parties will interact with each other more often. While the two parties may be in the same industry, they have different operational standards that can entail varying tasks and processes. These companies will respect one another's duties and will not try to undermine each other.

3. Precompetitive Alliance

Sometimes the alliance can entail an intense amount of conflict. A precompetitive alliance entails more conflict while having less interaction in the process. The two entities are typically from different fields and are working together to reach a common goal.

4. Competitive Alliance

A competitive alliance is when the two parties involved are in the same industry and could be interpreted as rivals. These two may be opposed to one another, but they might have similar goals or desires that will require them to link together and be more competitive.

Your competitive alliance can entail any of these four points. You can check on your partner and see if that entity is in your field or is competitive against you in any way. Don't assume you can't enter a partnership with someone opposed to you somehow, because there's always a chance that party will want to stick with you and support your work needs.

Planning a Partnership the Right Way

Your strategic partnership with a safety material provider can help you keep your costs down, plus it establishes a positive relationship built on trust. You can use these steps to establish a smart partnership:

1. Be specific when talking about why you want to enter a partnership.

Explain the assets you have and how the other party can benefit from what you hold. The other party will be more likely to enter a partnership if it knows what you have is something it can use.

You should have a business plan or vision statement for your work ready before attempting to enter a partnership. Figure out your needs to see what fits your business before you start.

2. Review why your potential partner would want to enter a partnership.

Your possible partner might have a desire to enter a partnership, but that group's requirements may be different from what you hold. Review what the party is saying, and figure out if you have a shared vision that fits. The relationship should be beneficial to both parties, but that only works if both sides have a good idea of what they want and their desires match in some way.

3. Create a follow-up meeting for your work.

A suitable follow-up plan can help you confirm the details of your partnership. The process of establishing a partnership should include multiple meetings where you hash out everything. Both sides must be on the same page and ready to plan the work, so follow-up meetings will be necessary for going forward.

4. Put all agreements down in words. Keep records of everything you say.

Keep all agreements in writing to confirm the terms of your partnership. Keep the points simple without being hard or otherwise unmanageable. You can request you keep the details in writing to confirm your interests while preserving everyone's ideas. These points can also help you in legal situations where there might be disputes over what is happening in an agreement.

5. You can expand the partnership to include more parties later.

Both sides in the partnership can welcome more parties later, but there should be defined rules over what the partnerships will entail. Both sides should equally agree upon whoever will enter the group, as disputes could make it harder for the team to grow and succeed.

Everything you do when planning an agreement will be essential to figuring out how your partnership will work. The partnership should last for years and be worthwhile for whatever needs your business holds.

Purchasing Consortium

Another option you have for handling workplace safety involves planning a purchasing consortium. A consortium is an association of multiple businesses working together to achieve a goal.

A purchasing consortium allows multiple businesses to acquire assets for safety purposes. They can do this to keep their costs for acquiring assets down.

The reason a purchasing consortium is cheaper comes from how these businesses will buy more assets for safety purposes at a time. Since there are more items involved, these businesses can potentially obtain a volume discount.

For instance, if a group of people purchased up to $7,499 of safety materials, the group would pay regular prices for these assets. But if they bought anywhere from $7,500 to $14,999 of those assets, these groups would get a 10 percent discount. Meanwhile, an order of $15,000 or more could include a 20 percent discount.

These companies would save money because they're pooling their resources to acquire similar items at a discount. You will not pay as much because you're benefitting from the volume discount that comes from acquiring so many things.

It's also easier to complete your orders, as the larger consortium can streamline the ordering effort. Since there is one party requesting items, it becomes easier for the transaction to move forward. The consortium can list multiple addresses for shipping items to different places.

Everyone can also establish a better relationship with the vendor. The vendor will be more responsive in handling everyone's needs. The consortium will have more purchasing power because there is more money involved and multiple parties in that group. Therefore, the vendor will want to keep one's promises while providing a better deal for services.

One good example of a purchasing consortium involves the <u>Big Ten Academic Alliance</u>. This organization consists of universities that are members of the Big Ten athletic conference. One school handles the solicitation process for acquiring assets and materials for academic projects and activities between the schools. The consortium allows these universities to handle their expenses without substantial losses.

How Do You Prepare a Purchasing Consortium?

You can establish a purchasing consortium with various parties, but the process of getting people together can be daunting.

You can use these steps to prepare a purchasing consortium:

1. Look for information on other businesses that require the same safety assets as what you require.

You can check online for different businesses in your industry to see who could use these items. While you could try contacting your direct competitors, they may not be willing to agree to enter the same consortium as you.

The similarities should be as precise as possible. You don't want to enter a deal where someone might need too many different things, as you might not qualify for volume discounts if the orders you plan are too different.

2. Check the terms of your purchasing consortium and prepare a suitable sales pitch based on what you find.

Explain to potential partners that your consortium will produce lower prices for safety materials thanks to volume discounts. Talk about why these assets are ideal for everyone's safety needs.

3. List all the vendors you're going to include.

There's no limit to how many vendors you can hire. You could contact one group for PPE and another for guard rails, ladders, and other safety materials. Explain what each vendor does and what types of assets they provide, plus list some of the possible purchases people can make.

The listing can include wholesalers for cases where businesses want items they want to acquire for resale. While most safety materials will likely be used by the businesses themselves, expect some parties to want to acquire wholesale items for their benefit.

4. Figure out how the group will be funded.

All members will need to pay an administration fee to enter the consortium. Keep the fee sensible, and avoid producing something too expensive to where no one will save anything.

5. Warehousing may be necessary, so list what you can get out of it.

Warehousing can help in cases where items will go to multiple addresses. An order can be drop-shipped to one party, and that entity can then send out assets to other people in the consortium based on when they need them and where they will go. Find suitable warehouse space and figure out the costs you'd have to cover to handle the warehousing effort.

6. List the savings people will attain when they join the group.

Try to come up with specific numbers on how much people will save. Other parties will be more likely to join your group if they know how much they're going to keep in the consortium.

You can consult as many people as you wish when getting your purchasing consortium ready. They'll be willing to enter if they have enough information on how your consortium works and what they can expect.

How Do You Fund the Purchasing Consortium?

Your will fund your purchasing consortium through administration fees. The fees are based on the price of whatever items people acquire, but a one-time fee may also work. The charge helps manage administrative or record-keeping costs, plus you can cover applicable warehousing costs when necessary.

You can set an administration fee at any value, but it should be reasonable enough to where it's not too expensive or cost-prohibitive to where people might not be willing to join the consortium.

Determine when planning your administration fees if you're going to make them one-time fees or charges that make up a percentage of the order. Anything you design should be rational enough to where potential members will want to join your group and feel better about what's open here.

You can also establish terms for how long people would have to stick in a consortium. The best idea is to have no minimums for how long people can stay in the consortium, but you could also charge fees to anyone who wants to leave the consortium.

Whatever you do, make sure you keep the consortium rules specific and direct. Avoid using complex language, and make sure it's easier for you to manage your details well enough.

Using Recruiters

Recruiters are among the best people you can have at your workplace. A recruiter will find, screen, and bring in applicants who want to apply for open positions. Recruiters will find the best possible candidates for whatever job openings are available in your workplace, giving you more help growing your business.

Recruiters are available in many forms, with safety recruiters being among the most viable ones you can hire today. A safety recruiter will interview and select qualified candidates for jobs relating to safety in your business.

Safety recruiters are ideal to hire for your business, as they help you fill positions while ensuring you find the best possible candidates. You'll save money because you won't struggle to hire people that might not always work. It's easier for a safety recruiter to hire the right person the first time around, keeping you from spending more to hire someone.

Recruiters may also have an easier time reviewing possible employees. The recruiter can learn about what needs your business holds and find a plan for work that fits.

What Functions Will a Safety Recruiter Manage?

A safety recruiter should be trained in understanding how to handle safety measures and how to find people who can manage safety-related processes.

The safety recruiter will focus on filling positions based on safety standards. The recruiter should be certified in managing OSHA and ISO standards for safety. The person can also analyze your business and determine what safety standards are necessary to follow for success.

The recruiter will analyze your job opening, prepare a suitable job posting, and then check which potential employees are right for you. The goal is to find someone who fits your workplace culture and can handle whatever safety standards you're trying to plan.

The Recruiter's Process

The recruiter uses a simple process for finding workers, but you'll have to put in some effort to help your recruiter. Here's a process for hiring a worker:

1.   You will open the initial position.

You'll provide information to the recruiter on the position you want to fill. List everything surrounding your job opening, including specifics on why you're hiring someone for that spot.

2.   The recruiter will analyze the position and create a listing.

The listing will include all the details you provided. Sometimes the job posting can appear on social media pages.

3.   The recruiter posts the listing on various platforms.

Traditional job sites are useful, but a safety recruiter will look for suitable job boards that fit your opening's standards. The safety recruiter could also post open jobs on your company website or that recruiter's portal.

Some social media sites can also work, but they should be ones relevant to the opening. LinkedIn is the most common social media site where recruiters can post openings, as LinkedIn is more professional than other social media spaces.

4.   The recruiter checks all the applications.

One reason you'll save money on hiring is that you'll allow the recruiter to check all the applications you receive, helping you save time and money on recruiting plans. It is estimated that a typical job opening can bring in at least 200 resumes or applications, while less than five percent of those people will be called for a job interview. It could take weeks for someone to get a job offer after applying for a position.

The recruiter will check each application to see what experiences workers have, how they can adhere to safety standards, and what technical skills they hold. All workers should be analyzed to see how well they can meet safety standards and rules in the workplace.

5.   The recruiter also interviews potential candidates.

The recruiter can choose which people are best for the job and conduct interviews with them. In-person or by-phone interviews can work, although reviews through online video portals can also work.

The interview process lets the recruiter learn more about each candidate. The candidates can provide answers to questions, plus they may show some appealing personality traits different from what others might expect.

The interview is about comparing hard and soft skills with one another. Hard skills refer to the job-related knowledge someone holds, while soft skills are the personal qualities a person has that could help someone succeed.

Recruiters can talk with candidates about work and life experiences, career goals, and desires for work. The information a recruiter gathers in an interview can be more details than what you might find in a resume.

6. Feedback from the interview is analyzed.

The feedback from the interview will include an analysis of the good and bad qualities surrounding the worker. Everything is compared to the needs you have for your job.

7. The most appealing job candidates will receive job offers.

Your recruiter will provide job offers to the people you want to hire. The recruiter is a liaison between you and the possible employee. The recruiter will negotiate the terms of employment with the new employee and help get that person on board.

This step also involves the recruiter informing other candidates that the position was filled. The recruiter will let these people know that other job openings may be available in the future, and those people will be encouraged to apply for those positions when available.

8. The recruiter will stay in touch with your new employees during a probation period.

The length of the probation period at the workplace can vary, but it is necessary for identifying possible problems and issues. The recruiter can be a mediator who can manage relationships with your new employees.

Staying in touch with your recruiter can help you manage your hiring plans well and ensure you're hiring the right people. You can enjoy a long-term relationship with a quality safety recruiter if you're on the same page with that someone.

Three Forms of Hiring

A safety recruiter can help you find employees in one of three forms:

1. Temporary staff

Temporary safety staff members can work for your business for a brief time to help manage the implementation of safety standards. These people can work during renovation or construction projects, for example. You can also bring in people who can help install new devices and materials.

2. Temp to hire

The temp to hire process involves hiring a person for a limited time and then having the option to give that person a permanent position in the workplace after the timeframe ends. You could provide a permanent role to the temp worker if you are satisfied with how well the worker performs. Any worker who fits the workplace culture well will also be beneficial to your work plans.

3.   Direct hire

A direct hire occurs when you directly hire a person without putting someone in a temp position. The candidate will officially become a permanent employee and will go on your payroll while also receiving whatever benefits you offer.

Check your needs for workers to see who you can hire and what types of positions you need to fill. Look at how well you're going to need someone, and make a plan that fits well enough. Be sure the plan also fits your long-term needs, as you might require certain employees to stick around for a while.

What Does It Cost to Hire a Safety Recruiter?

It is more affordable for a business to manage safety standards when it hires people who understand how safety works. The cost of hiring a safety recruiter is also more efficient than you may expect, as paying for a recruiter helps make the hiring process more effective and straightforward.

A typical safety recruiter will charge about **15 to 20 percent of the worker's first-year salary** after you fill a permanent job. The total could go **up to 25 to 30 percent if the position is high-end or otherwise tough to fill**. The value could also shift based on the industry, market conditions, and unique specifics surrounding the position.

For example, you might hire a safety recruiter to fill a position with a first-year salary of $80,000. The recruiter could charge anywhere from $12,000 to $24,000 for the work.

Some recruiters may also work on an hourly basis. A recruiter might charge **$50 to $70 an hour** to screen candidates, plus it would cost $200 to $300 a week to post a job, review resumes, and conduct other administrative tasks. You could spend at least $10,000 to get one position filled in some situations.

The cost to hire someone can vary for temporary positions. For temp employees, the recruiter can charge an hourly rate where the recruiter gets a cut of the employee's hourly salary as long as that person stays employed. The recruiter also earns a transfer fee if the temp employee becomes a permanent one. The recruiter no longer gets the hourly salary cut, but the transfer fee will ensure the recruiter is properly compensated for the work the person did.

Expect the cost to be higher if you have more high-profile positions that require extra effort to fill. The positions where you'll require more analysis and candidates will cost extra, as there's a need to check each person in the talent pool to see who fits the task. But the cost can be worthwhile when you consider the duties and responsibilities the person will have. It's easier to save money on the recruiting cost when you have a recruiter who can find someone who won't leave too soon or demand more than necessary.

Why Hire a Recruiter Instead of Doing Things Yourself?

While the cost to hire a safety recruiter might sound substantial, you'll likely save money hiring a safety recruiter than if you tried hiring someone on your own without help.

National Business Capital writes that the cost to hire a safety recruiter can be daunting, but the cost to get a new staff member on board can also be high. You'll have to train your new workers and take care of all onboarding charges for getting a worker to receive health insurance benefits and other rewards for being an employee. These charges and training costs can make you pay 1.25 to 1.4 times the employee's salary over the first year.

Hiring people who will succeed without bearing with employee turnover is critical to keeping your business safe without spending money. A safety recruiter's work can reduce the risk of an employee leaving too soon, ensuring you won't waste more money than necessary on the hiring process.

PeopleKeep also says you'd have to spend more than 100 percent of an employee's salary on replacing a person if that someone leaves the workplace. That total can rise to 200 percent for high-end positions. The costs to hire a recruiter again, onboarding costs for a new worker, lost productivity due to someone leaving, and a drop in employee morale are all problems that can occur if people keep leaving your workplace. There might also be a negative cultural impact in the workplace, as people might start to think your workplace isn't thinking about safety.

It's also easier to fill in positions when you hire a safety recruiter. Since the recruiter has more understanding of how to hire someone, it is easier for that person to bring in someone than if you tried doing so yourself. Since there's less time involved in hiring someone, you won't waste money on hiring efforts and losing productivity because you were too busy trying to hire someone.

The long-term savings you'll get from hiring a safety recruiter will more than offset the short-term costs associated with bringing in that recruiter for help.

What If the Recruiter Cannot Find Anyone?

As useful as a safety recruiter can be for your workplace, there's always the potential that the recruiter won't be able to find anyone to fill in a position. The recruiter should provide terms where you will not be required to spend as much money if the recruiter is unsuccessful.

For instance, the recruiter can refund a substantial portion of the filing fees and other charges if no one can enter the position. The terms will vary by the recruiter, so you will likely have to spend money even if that person cannot hire anyone. But it won't be as expensive as you might assume.

Additional Tips For Hiring a Safety Recruiter

While hiring a safety recruiter is a smart idea, it is also more effective if you know what you're planning when bringing someone into the mix. There are a few steps you can use when hiring a safety recruiter you can trust for your work.

1. The recruiter you hire should have proper people skills.

Recruiters will spend much of their days interviewing people. Anyone you hire as a recruiter should be ready to talk with candidates and discuss things with them well enough. A recruiter should be interested in what the candidates have to say and ready to discuss different things as necessary.

2. The recruiter should be capable of juggling whatever job details you post.

Your job opening will include many details and points that might be tough for some people to figure out. Your recruiter should be ready to handle all the job details and points you post, making it easier for someone to interview others and compare candidates with the needs you hold.

3. Intuition makes a difference.

The best safety recruiters have good instincts that help them understand who will be safe on the job and how well that person might identify problems. The recruiter has to look at the candidate and figure out if that someone is smart enough and recognizes what is necessary for success.

4. Your recruiter can also take note of the rest of your team and compare your current staff with candidates.

A recruiter should check how your business operates and figure out how the vibe and attitude around your business are. The recruiter will notice the safety standards you follow and the details you manage to keep things safe. The worker can then compare all candidates with what's in your workplace now, helping see if the candidates can comply with your rules.

5. Flexibility is critical.

Flexibility is a necessity when recruiting people. A recruiter should be willing to adapt to the different needs your company holds. The business should be ready to go in new directions without sticking with past needs or demands for far too long. A recruiter who can switch priorities and needs will be more likely to find a worker for your opening.

6. Integrity is also vital.

The safety standards and other details in your business are critical to your operation. Your recruiter should keep your business info private and secure. You must keep compensation data and other reports secure from other people. Privacy is critical for ensuring nothing wrong will happen with the data your recruiter is being entrusted to handle.

9 Creating a Suitable Job Opening

This next point expands upon how a safety recruiter can work for you. While a recruiter can provide good results, you'll also have to be specific when planning a job opening.

The job openings you post can influence who will come onto your business. An opening that sticks around too long might cost more money to manage than necessary, as you'll struggle to find potential employees and spend more on marketing your positions than you expect.

But what makes this point essential for reducing workplace safety charges?

When managing workplace safety, you'll need to provide enough info to people on what is expected of them when keeping your business safe. Your job opening will include details on what people will do and how they're going to protect others. Candidates should know what to expect in the workplace and how well they're going to handle various tasks.

The job you promote should be one people will feel comfortable completing. They don't want to enter a workplace and be surprised by what they will find. They want something that is sensible and easy to plan for without being complex. Discussing the safety needs and plans in your workplace within your job listing will help people feel more confident in your position, and some people who might have been on the fence about applying will be more invested in the work position.

You can use a few points to help you create a sensible job opening listing that fits your business and includes sensible details that will work well.

Planning Your Overview

The job opening for your business will include an overview of everything the worker will handle. The opening should include details on what the worker will do in the workplace and how various safety measures and protocols will work.

The overview should cover things like these:

- What interactions workers will have with others, whether they entail other workers or customers
- Necessary qualifications, including any safety certifications or training courses one must complete
- Any assets the worker will require, including a valid driver's license or whatever necessary equipment you want the worker to provide
- The times when someone will work, including how many hours one might work and when those hours will occur
- Any seasonal or temporary tasks the worker might complete

Everything you explain in your interview should be clear and simple. Present tense terms help, plus bullet points can make your data easier to read.

Listing Salary Info

Money is an important need for many people, and many job seekers will look at salary info when finding something of value. They want to be assured they're being paid well for the work they w`1zrrovide. Therefore, you'll have to provide salary details within your listings.

You'll spend less money filling positions if you provide enough salary info to your candidates. People are more willing to respond to a job opening if they know the salaries available are more appealing. But the salary info you list should also be realistic. You don't want to promise something you might not be capable of providing.

Instead of listing a specific dollar amount, list a salary range. It can entail a range of how much someone could earn per hour or throughout the year. Instead of promising something at a time, you can instead get people an idea of what to expect.

Your salary info can also include a listing of whatever benefits someone might be entitled to during employment. These include medical, vision, and dental coverage.

Managing Adjectives the Right Way

The adjectives in your workplace listing can provide an expectation of what you will expect from your workers. You could say that someone is "properly organized," or you might ask someone to be "thorough and precise" when working.

Adjectives can help you explain what you want out of your workers, but make sure when using adjectives that you're describing your work environment well. Provide enough of an idea for seeing what fits and how well people can work in your business.

Be specific when discussing the adjectives you want to follow. For example, you might recommend that someone should be a "fast learner." But instead of saying that, you could also say that someone should be "ready to adapt to new activities in the workplace."

Everyone has different ideas about what certain adjectives mean. One person might think that "fast-paced environment" means "a place where someone will always be under pressure," but another may think it that means "a place where anything can happen." Think about what people might consider when looking at your adjectives, and plan whatever you want to say well to reduce confusion.

Explain Your Company Culture

Your job posting should also relate to your company's culture. You can include references to what your business goals are and how you're going to keep your company afloat. You can also list the beliefs you have when helping people and how you're going to serve your community well.

Your business may have a unique mission concentrating on providing a safe environment while being friendly. Explain your culture in your listing, and let people know what makes your work unique. You will help people understand what makes your business special when you see what works.

10

First Aid Training and Preparation on a Budget

First aid is vital to every business safety plans. While preventing workplace injuries and other issues from happening is critical, there are still times when first aid may be necessary.

For example, a person might collapse after becoming dehydrated while on the job. Someone might also have cut oneself with a simple office tool.

There's also the potential someone might have a heart attack or stroke while in your workplace. These medical emergencies can occur at any time and without warning. There's no way you can prevent every single emergency from happening, and you'll need to prepare for anything that might happen before anything becomes worse.

First aid training and preparation will be vital to keeping your workers safe and preventing medical issues from becoming worse. First aid promotes healing and allows your business to stay functional and afloat, as the risk of someone not being able to work for too long will become minimal.

It can take about ten to fifteen minutes for emergency authorities to arrive after calling them for help. The timing can be even longer in rural areas where they may not be as accessible. First aid training is vital for protecting people in the workplace and showing your commitment to keeping everyone in the workplace safe.

First aid training and preparation are easy to manage without spending much money. From refurbished materials to a proper first aid kit sized and rated based on your needs, you can find a safety plan that is affordable while keeping everyone protected. You will show people how responsible you are for safety when you have the right plans.

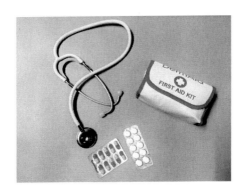

Basic First Aid Training

First aid training courses can cover many points on how to tend to people who are injured or require life-saving measures. These courses can help people learn how to help support people, especially in cases where you need to stabilize someone who is seriously injured or in a significant medical episode.

A first aid course will cover the OSHA First Aid standard of <u>29 CFR 1910.151</u>. Other countries outside the United States have different standards such as the <u>Health and Safety (First-Aid) Regulations 1981</u> in the United Kingdom or <u>Part XVI of Canada Occupational Health and Safety Regulations</u>. But all of these standards are similar to what OSHA uses.

The standard says first aid should be made available to any workplace of any size if there are no infirmaries or hospitals in the near proximity to the work environment.

A first aid training program can cover many points:

- How to recognize a medical emergency
- How to apply first aid materials as necessary
- How to communicate with emergency authorities when needed
- Reviewing different first aid materials
- How to handle a person's body during an emergency, including how to keep a person's body stable as necessary
- Specific treatments for children; this point is valid for workplaces where children may be present for any reason

A course can also cover how to manage non-life-threatening emergencies. Some of the points people can learn include:

- Treatment of cuts
- Infection treatment procedures
- How to handle sprains, strains, and cramps
- How to identify burn types
- Treating burns

You can check with various health and safety organizations to find training programs in your area. These include group training sessions that support multiple people in your workplace.

A typical first aid training course can go from $25 to $40 per person. You may qualify for volume discounts if you have multiple people completing the course.

You don't have to worry about traveling to some location to complete a first aid course either. A training organization can come to your business and provide on-site training to everyone.

The Red Cross organization in your country is the most prominent group that offers first aid training courses. You can check around online to find other standard-approved first aid certification courses. The cost for first aid training will remain the same in most situations regardless of who you contact for help.

CPR Certification

CPR certification is also available through various health organizations like the American Heart Association and American, British, or Canadian Red Cross. CPR or cardiopulmonary resuscitation is a treatment for people suffering cardiac arrest.

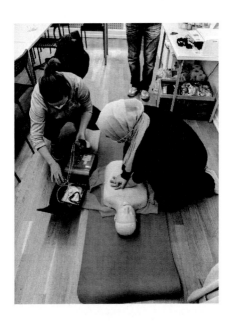

CPR involves chest compressions and artificial ventilation to help restore blood circulation and breathing when someone experiences cardiac arrest. CPR helps preserve brain and heart function and will support the patient's health while waiting for emergency authorities to arrive and provide further support.

CPR is critical for saving a person's life, as it can take a while for proper medical authorities to reach an area. Your employees can undergo CPR certification to help them stay safe.

The CPR training process will cover many points:

- The signs of a heart attack or stroke
- How to clear the patient's airway
- How to apply chest compressions
- Proper rescue breathing into the patient's mouth to restore breathing
- How to handle one and two-person rescue procedures

The cost for CPR certification will vary by provider, but it can cost about $40 to $60 for a person to undergo training. Training materials can also cost about $20 to $30 to use. Volume discounts may be available for all the workers in your space. A CPR trainer may also come to your site to train people, so everyone in the workplace can learn together.

Online training is also available, as it helps your workers from anywhere and doesn't require classroom training. But the cost for online training will be almost the same as what classroom-based training costs, as all people will still have to complete in-person testing to receive certification.

AED Use

Another item for first aid your business will require is an automated external defibrillator or AED. An AED is a portable material that will deliver a shock to the patient's body. The shock helps restore the heart's natural rhythm.

An AED unit can include voice prompts or other instructions for the user. You can place the pads over the patient's body, and the AED will review the patient's heart rhythm. The device then lets you know when you need to administer a shock.

CPR training programs will often include AED training at no additional cost. You will learn how to administer a shock with an AED, including where to apply the shock, how often the shock is necessary, and when you need to administer it.

AED use can increase the likelihood of a person surviving cardiac arrest. An AED should be used within the first three minutes after a person collapses from cardiac arrest, as any situation where the heart isn't defibrillated before then could lead to death.

Be prepared to review the cost of your AED device when adding it to your workplace. An AED can cost anywhere from $1,000 to $2,500 to acquire.

You'll have to replace the AED battery on occasion as well. The battery can cost about $200 to $500 and last for about two to five years on average while on standby mode.

The AED pads should also be replaced every 18 to 30 months. The pads will cost about $50 to $100 to replace.

You can always find a refurbished AED device for about half the cost of a new one. A refurbished model will meet all standards and will undergo testing and certification to ensure it functions well. You could spend less than $1,000 on an AED, but make sure everything is inspected and tested well before going forward with your order.

Don't forget about the storage cabinet. A wall storage cabinet can cost about $100 to $150 to purchase. The cabinet should be locked and placed in an unobstructed area for easy access, plus the cabinet key should be labeled and stored in a safe place to keep it from being lost. The cabinet should also be about 48 inches over the floor to allow anyone to access it.

In summary, you could spend up to $3,000 on an AED, but a refurbished one and the necessary storage space can be available for about $1,000.

While the cost of an AED might be high for some, it is necessary to administer an AED to patients at times. The odds of someone surviving a sudden cardiac event will drop if defibrillation is delayed for too long.

But be advised when finding an AED that you're finding one that has full approval from the Food and Drug Administration. The FDA requires all AEDs to be approved for medical use, as AEDs are interpreted by the FDA as medical devices.

The FDA also does not regulate resuscitation guidelines for using AEDs. Proper education on how to use an AED is necessary. You can learn how to use an AED during a first aid training course.

First Aid Kits

Your business will require a first aid kit to manage injuries. The first aid kit will include all the materials necessary for treating common workplace injuries.

The American National Standards Institute encourages businesses to have first aid kits that meet <u>ANSI Z308.1-2015</u> standards. Similar standards are also used in various other countries, as they entail providing enough assets in a first aid kit.

These standards include two different types of first aid kits:

1. **Class A** – For common injuries
2. **Class B** – For more specific injuries or use in high-risk environments

The materials in Class A and B first aid kits are about the same, except a Class B first aid kit will include more quantities of certain items.

Your first aid kit will require these assets:

- Adhesive bandages of 1 x 3 inches
- 2.5 yards of adhesive tape
- Antibiotic application

- Antiseptic
- Burn dressing of 4 x 4 inches
- Burn treatment materials
- A cold pack at 4 x 5 inches
- Eye or skin wash
- Hand sanitizer materials
- Medical exam gloves
- Scissors
- Sterile pads of 3 x 3 inches
- Trauma pad of 5 x 9 inches

These materials can be arranged in compartments that are color-coordinated based on the materials inside them. Yellow compartments are for bandages, while red containers are for burn treatment, for instance.

All Class A and B first aid kits can also be in one of four types:

1. **Type I** – A stationary kit for indoor applications with a minimal amount of environmental risks
2. **Type II** – For portable indoor use
3. **Type III** – For portable indoor or outdoor use; a water-resistant seal is necessary
4. **Type IV** – For outdoor or mobile situations where the potential for damages due to environmental factors is high

A compliant first aid kit will not cost much to purchase. A Class A first aid kit can be found for $40 to $100, with higher type variants costing more.

A Class B first aid kit will cost more at $60 to $150, as the kit has more materials and will take up more space.

The kit you purchase should be planned based on your business size and how you operate. A less expensive Class A first aid kit that meets Type I standards will be ideal for smaller and less active workplaces, for instance. Choosing the right kit based on your usage needs and environment can keep you from spending more on it than you may require.

You can also order refills for the items in your first aid kit as necessary, including when you run out of items or some things inside it go past their shelf lives. The refills will cost about half as much as the initial cost of a first aid kit. All items should be kept in sterile and sealed packages so you can add them to your first aid kit. You can order these refills as necessary, but check your kit on occasion to see how it has its items and if you need to complete a reorder.

First Aid Kit Usage Form

One way you can save money on your first aid kit is by keeping tabs on how often people use it. You can prepare a first aid kit usage form that keeps track of when people use your first aid kit.

The Boretti, Inc. Business Safety Solutions company has a free first aid kit usage form you can download and use for your workplace. It includes a form where employees can list:

- When they used the first aid kit
- What items were removed
- Why these items were necessary

The supervisor can sign off on these uses to confirm they are in the company's records. By using this form, you will keep from reordering items too soon. You don't want to keep too many items on hand, as some compounds only have a limited shelf life. Storing too many things at once could also increase the risk of the sterile protective packaging for these items being opened.

11

Safety Equipment and PPE

Safety and personal protective equipment or PPE have never been more essential to today's working world. The global pandemic that started in 2020 showed how important it is for everyone to be kept safe and secure from transmissible diseases and other threats.

While the pandemic may be weakening its grip on the world as of the summer of 2022, the need for safety equipment and PPE is still essential. Businesses are learning how vital it is to have such materials on hand to protect their workers and keep them safe from various outside threats.

Today's PPE industry has been growing, as you can find various items for every need. But you'll need to know what your workers will require and figure out precise amounts for your business needs. PPE can be affordable when you know what your business requires while making the right purchasing plans.

But the PPE industry is vast, as there are many PPE materials you could use in your workplace today. You'll have to find the right PPE product by comparing different items with one another. Some PPE products look similar, but they have different functions. Others are more appropriate for specific situations or industries.

Simple or Complex?

The first part of planning your PPE efforts involves reviewing whether you need simple or complex PPE.

Simple personal protective equipment is a basic type of PPE material. It is suitable for low-risk hazards, including ones where the users will easily recognize the risks in the workplace. People can make assessments in identify what PPE is necessary, with simple equipment suitable in most situations.

Complex PPE is a different material, as it is more technical and specific. Complex PPE is for when users cannot identify risks in enough time. It is also for situations where the hazards are more dramatic and require further protection.

Complex PPE costs more than simple PPE, as complex materials are designed for heavy-duty use. You could spend two or three times as much money on complex PPE equipment as you'd spend on simple materials. Look at the potential risks in your workplace and figure out a plan for what you're going to bring out.

Skin Protection

There are many forms of PPE you can use in the workplace. First, let's look at skin protection.

Skin protection is available in separate, apron, and overall forms. Separate skin protection materials cover a part of the body, while aprons cover the front part. Overalls, boiler suits, chemical suits, and other similar items cover the entire body. Some items are reusable, while others are disposable.

Other forms of skin protection include knee and elbow pads, gaiters for the shins, and metal guards that can go over the body to protect the user from impacts.

The cost for skin protection can vary surrounding how much of the body is being covered. PPE shirts can cost about **$10 to $20 each**, while aprons can go for **$10 to $30**. Coveralls can go for about **$40 or higher**. All of these items can be washed as necessary, although the costs for cleaning materials can vary depending on what you prefer to use. The PPE may also last for only a few washes, although the lifespan of these items can vary based on how often you use them and the environments you enter.

Disposable materials are helpful for situations where people are in hazardous environments where it is too risky to wear the same thing multiple times. You could spend about half as much on these skin protection materials as you would on non-disposable items, but you'd have to review how often people would wear these items and when you'd have to replace these features.

Respiratory Materials

Respiratory materials are vital for people who work in environments where the air quality may be dangerous. Respiratory items prevent materials from entering the mouth. They also go over the mouth and other nearby parts, allowing thorough protection and keeping the workers' airways safe.

There are two common types of respiratory materials available:

1. Filtered Face Mask

A traditional filtered face mask will filter out contaminated materials from the air.

These disposable masks are relatively affordable, as a pack of 50 can be found for about **$5 to $10 on average.**

2. Full-Face Respirator

A full-face respirator can be reusable and may offer additional eye protection. The device can include cartridges that can help filter out particles. This model is more detailed and works best for situations where people are in hazardous areas for long periods or where the hazards are more serious to where a regular filtered face mask may not be suitable enough.

Full-face respirators can go from $120 to $300, while replacement filter cartridges can cost about $20 to $30. These items work best when you have ongoing work needs that require more protection.

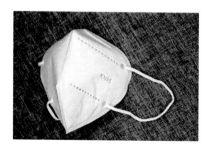

The Difference Between N95, KN95, and KF94

Three of the more common face masks you may find when looking for PPE are N95, KN95, and KF94 masks.

N95 masks are the most common ones you'll find. The N95 term means it can filter at least 95 percent of airborne particles that are 0.3 microns or larger in size. It is also a non-oil mask that is safe in areas where no oil-based particulates are present.

KN95 masks are similar to N95 masks, but they feature ear hooks that are easier to manage than what traditional N95 masks use. The KN95 model is also easier to fold for storage use, plus you can apply a secondary filter to a KN95 mask. These filters are best when you use them once. KN95 masks work better in situations where you encounter multiple people at a time or are in close quarters.

A KF94 mask is easier to wear in most situations, as it is available in more sizes and uses secure hooks for securing the mask behind your ears. But it also has a lower effectiveness rate, as it filters about 94 percent of airborne particles.

The good news is there isn't much difference in how much these masks cost. A pack of 100 disposable N95 masks can go for **$25**, while KF94 masks will cost about the same.

KN95 masks can go for about **$25 to $50 for 100 of them**, plus it will cost at least **$20 for 100 replacement filters** for these masks. The need to use these masks in closer environments with less room for movement is part of why these masks cost more on average.

Eyewear is necessary for many workplace environments, including ones where the air may contain gases or other items that might irritate the eyes. Eyewear provides a secure fit over the eyes, allowing the mucus membranes to stay safe without experiencing possible irritation. You can also use eyewear in environments where particles and other foreign objects might fly around an area.

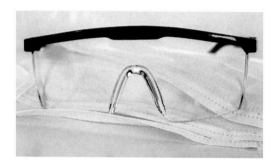

PPE eyewear can last for a while, although it can be disposed of after enough time. The lifespan of the eyewear can vary over how long some uses it and what types of environments it is used in. Each person might have different needs for PPE eyewear, so ordering plenty of copies of something and having them ready for when people need them is ideal.

There are three types of PPE eyewear you can order:

1.   Safety Glasses

Safety glasses are useful for workplaces where people encounter flying objects. They are not intended for dust or vapors, as these glasses will not cover all parts of the eyes.

Safety glasses cost less than others, with some being available for **80 to 90 cents each when purchased in bulk.**

2. Goggles

Safety goggles provide more coverage than safety glasses. Goggles feature guards that go on the sides of the face and create a seal that protects the eyes from vapors and dust. There's also a band on the end that helps you keep a secure fit.

Safety goggles are convenient and often include adjustable straps that can fit anyone's head, but these will cost extra. Expect to spend about **$10 to $15 for each pair** of safety goggles.

3. Face Visor

A face visor will go over the entire face. It covers the whole face and allows a person with prescription glasses to wear it without obstruction. Some visors also include flip-up designs where you can raise the visor as necessary.

Face visors are cheap, as you can find them for **$3 to $5 each** when you order them in bulk. But anything you order should feature reinforced materials that will keep them intact. Anti-fogging visors are also ideal, as these will not cloud up as a person breathes while using them.

The face visor should also have a secure design where the material is easy to handle.

What About Prescription Materials?

Prescription PPE eyewear is available in many situations, but it will cost more to order these glasses. Prescription safety glasses can cost about **$50 to $100**, depending on how the lenses are prepared. You can order specific glasses for certain people who require prescriptions, although they may require eye exams to confirm their prescriptions.

As for goggles, make sure any goggles you order are sized well to where a person's regular glasses will not get in the way. Even then, it may be best to have someone wear prescription PPE safety glasses under those goggles.

Safety Helmets

Safety helmets are also vital for protection, especially in workplaces where falling objects may be present. People in the construction industry will benefit from these PPE products the most.

Today's industrial safety helmets are available for **about $15 to $30 each when bought in bulk.** But you'll need to find a suitable safety helmet that fits well and is safe. The materials on the outside should be reinforced and sturdy, plus there should be enough padding on the inside to keep the helmet comfortable while staying in its position.

The strap on a helmet should also be sturdy enough to keep it in place. Adjustable straps can create a good fit, but they shouldn't become loose.

Additional Items For Your Safety Helmets

You can add many items to your safety helmets, but they will cost extra.

You can add a chin strap to a helmet, for example. Chin straps are available for **$2 to $5 each** and can add a reinforced fit to the helmet for windy conditions.

Headlamps are also available for helmets in dark environments. Such lamps can **cost $50 each** on average, but they are battery-powered models that are reinforced to where the batteries and bulbs won't break or become exposed.

What About Bump Caps?

Not every business has to spend money on full-size helmets. A bump cap is helpful for workplaces where the risk of falling objects is minimal, but there's also a risk of people bumping into various spaces. For example, maintenance personnel can use bump caps to keep them from hurting themselves when bumping into pipes, machines, and other items inside tightly-kept environments.

A bump cap comes with a smaller body and can fit underneath many head coverings. It can cost about **$5 to $10 each when ordered in bulk**, making it more affordable than a traditional helmet.

Look at the head injury risk in your workplace when figuring out if someone needs a bump cap. Check if falling objects are a threat, and look at the environment to see how close someone might be to various items. A bump cap will be good enough when the risks in an area aren't strong but still require further protection for everyone. Anything where falling items are too common or the risks are too dramatic will require you to stick with traditional helmets instead.

Ear Protection

Ear protection is essential for workplaces where noise can be a problem. Whether the noises come from machines and devices or crowded environments, ear protection can help.

The type of ear protection you use can cost a decent amount of money, with the more thorough and comprehensive options costing more. Here are three options to note:

1.   Ear Plugs

Ear plugs are basic ear protection devices that fit into the ear canal to create a seal. Such plugs can come with cords to help you keep them in your ears without risking them slipping out.

A plug works by having someone push down on a plug and then insert it into the ear canal. The plug then expands while in the canal to create a seal that keeps noises from getting into the canal.

Regular ear plugs can cost about **$10 to $20 for 100 pairs**. These plugs are intended for single use.

2.   Canal Caps

Canal caps are banded ear plugs where the plugs are connected to cords. These can go for **$10 to $20 for about 100 sets of them**. These ear plugs are ideal for situations where you need to remove them on occasion. But since these are easier to add and remove, they will not provide as much protection.

3. Ear Muffs

Industrial ear muffs are ideal for environments that are very loud or have noises that keep going for a while. Ear muffs come with sound-absorbing materials that keep excess noises from entering the ears. These muffs also have padded bodies that cover the entire ear, offering more protection.

Industrial ear muffs are often adjustable, as the user can tilt the ends up and down as necessary. The band at the top can also be expanded or contracted to provide a better fit. A small bit of padding can also appear on the top part for the user's comfort.

The intense protection provided by ear muffs makes them more expensive. You'll spend about **$10 per ear muff set on average.**

Check the intensity of the sounds in your workplace to determine what ear protection is necessary before making a purchase. Anything that might be too loud or might persist for a while will require ear muffs, while something less intense or frequent can be managed with ear plugs.

Look at whether people can avoid these loud noises if possible. It is possible to avoid some of these noises by checking on how your machines are maintained or what procedures you might use. But for cases where people have to be near noisy things, you'll have to get the right ear protection for the work.

Safety Shoes and Boots

You don't have to provide every single bit of PPE to your workers, although that is strongly recommended. For instance, you can ask them to foot the bill for some items, with safety shoes being a good example. Having them pay for their own shoes can help, as you'll give your workers more control over what shoes they'll wear while letting them determine which sizes they'll require the most.

But you may still need to ask a person what size shoe one wears first, as you might still have to pay for safety shoes yourself. You could spend anywhere from $50 to $100 for a pair of safety shoes or boots, plus you'd have to sort out your purchases based on what sizes you're trying to order.

But the benefits of safety shoes will make their costs worthwhile. Safety shoes and boots are useful for workers because they come with sturdy materials that protect the feet:

- The toe caps will be reinforced to keep the toes safe from dropping items and bumps.
- The midsoles will resist penetration, which is necessary when people walk on rough surfaces.

- The soles will feature slip-resistant materials that keep the user from falling in an area.
- Secure shoes can also resist shocks. This feature is necessary for environments where electric currents and other threats might become a problem.

Regardless of whether you or your employees pay for these shoes, you'll find these shoes through various stores. These shoes are available through in-person and online stores alike. Companies like New Balance, Skechers, Dr. Martens, Rocky, CAT, Work Master, and Red Wing make safety shoes and boots, with many of them available for **$100 or less**. Most places that sell shoes will have some selection of work shoes.

Contact your employees about what they need out of their shoes first, as you might not know what sizes they wear. Some workers will also want to know ahead of time if the shoes they'll wear on the job are comfortable and easy to manage.

There's also the option to contact a wholesaler for help in finding work shoes. But you'd have to figure out what sizes everyone wears first.

You could also recommend boots made with rubber or other flexible materials. These are called Wellington boots and can go up to right below a person's knees. But it's still ideal to only buy these when you're finding something interesting. In addition to such rubber boots costing $100 or more, there's the need to ensure these boots can fit the person's legs and feet well.

Gloves

Gloves are helpful for situations where people will contact multiple items with their hands while they work. Gloves can prevent blisters from forming around the hands, plus they can keep splinters and burns from being a threat.

The price for gloves will vary surrounding their designs. Basic work gloves can cost **$2 to $4 per pair**, while gloves that feature cuffs will go for **$5 to $8 per pair**. Any of these gloves will also cost more money if they cover more parts of the skin.

Secure gloves can last for a while, but make sure you have enough gloves on hand for everyone. Spares are necessary, as gloves can tear apart and become worn after enough use. You can also get extra gloves to cover cases where someone loses their pairs, as these items are easy to lose.

General Recommendations For All PPE Items

All of these PPE items can be useful, but they must be used correctly to ensure they last longer. You won't spend as much money on PPE if you maintain everything well.

Here are a few things to do to prolong the life of all PPE items to keep from having to replace them as often:

- Anything people wear should be suitable for the hazard. Avoid wearing things in environments where they aren't recommended or suitable.
- Always follow the manufacturer's instructions on how to use PPE. Avoid using it for longer than a recommended breakthrough time, for instance. Using something for too long can keep the PPE from being effective enough, or it might weaken faster.
- Store anything that was worn or otherwise contaminated separately from other items.

- Review everything for surface damage. Possible damages can keep the materials from being as effective.
- All PPE should be secure-fitting. Anything loose-fitting could be caught on various items, including moving machinery.
- Have enough backup copies of PPE items for cases where someone's PPE breaks or is damaged, a person misplaces something, or someone is in a more intense situation where the PPE might wear faster.

Buying PPE the Right Way

You'll have to buy almost all the PPE materials for your employees. While requesting them to buy their shoes and some other items might help, not all employees are willing to react well to this recommendation. Therefore, buying PPE materials yourself will be ideal.

The best way to buy PPE is to know precisely what you require before completing your order. You can complete a volume purchase to help you spend less money on each PPE item, as vendors will sell their items in bulk for less per piece.

A purchasing consortium can also help, as you can get in touch with other businesses that also want to buy workplace safety items. Everyone in a consortium can get together and buy items in greater bulk quantities for better deals. The consortium can also use a simple approach to administering assets to make things easy to manage.

There are a few other solutions to spot when getting PPE ready for your workplace:

1. Ask any supplier you contact about estimates for your order, including shipping and delivery times.

Make sure you know exactly what you're going to spend before going forward with an order.

2. Ask for a sample of the equipment beforehand. Check the sample to see what the product is like and if it will meet your needs. This step works well when seeing how something works before placing a massive order.

3. Ask for references from a vendor. You can learn from references if the materials you're ordering are reliable.

Your PPE orders will be vital for protecting everyone in your workplace. You must have the right PPE to keep everyone safe, but be careful when making purchases. You'll require enough materials for everyone while having backups to ensure everyone stays safe. Take note of the types of PPE available and which items might be the most suitable for your workplace.

12 Fall Protection Items

Workplaces that entail vast heights and fall hazards will require the right fall protection items to keep everyone safe. Whether they entail warehouses, construction sites, or any other wide-open areas, fall protection equipment is critical to maintaining a safe environment.

The risk of a fall at the workplace can be dramatic, as a fall can occur for many reasons. It might happen due to malfunctioning equipment or sudden weather conditions.

Some areas in the workplace might have open spots where someone could fall. OSHA states that any workplace that has fall hazards that are high enough are places that will require proper OSHA-approved fall protection. These include general industry sites with fall hazards at elevations of four feet, six-foot elevations at construction sites, five feet at shipyards, and eight feet at longshoring sites.

OSHA insists all companies with such fall hazards provide safe working conditions while providing the necessary fall protection materials. You can use various items to keep your business safe, plus you won't spend lots of money getting these fall protection assets ready.

But you'll also have to plan these workplace safety materials based on your needs to ensure you have protective items that won't harm your budget. Here are a few points to see for each of the fall protection items available for your worksite.

Note: All guidelines listed by OSHA are suitable for use in other countries, but the specific rules may vary by state or province. Check your local regulations for details on what works in your situation.

Guard Rails

OSHA requirements state guard rails should be included on every open-sided platform or floor. You can also add guard rails around machines that might be too dangerous to reach at times. These rails should be high enough for people to see. They should also have bright paint on them so people can see and distinguish them from a distance.

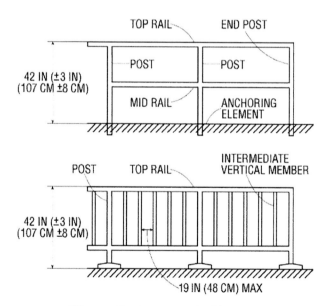

Figure D-11 Guardrail Systems

Guard rails can reduce costs from injuries, downtime, and machine damage.

OSHA requires a few things out of guard rails:

- A guard rail should be 42 inches high. A 3-inch tolerance is accepted.
- The guard rail should be above the walking surface.
- The rail must also be reinforced to handle at least 200 pounds of weight from any direction.

OSHA's standards for how guard rails work include rules for how many posts can work on the body. The guard rail can include multiple poles in the middle, although there should be less than 19 inches or 48 cm in between those spots. The openings should be small enough to keep items from slipping past a guard rail and getting in the way of something.

You can plan your guard rails by measuring the spaces where rails will be necessary. Look around machines and open areas to find spaces where people could fall or get too close to something if a guard rail isn't present.

After calculating the number of feet of guard rail space you'll require, you can choose a railing material. Steel is the most common item, although aluminum and carbon fiber can also work.

Look for the places where the guard rails will be installed. Parts of the floor will have to be dug up to support the posts where the rails will go.

A guard rail can cost about **$80 to $100 per foot** on average. Labor costs also go for about $30 per foot.

Toe Boards

While a guard rail can be essential, the bottom part near the rail will require a board that keeps rolling items from falling. A toe board will go under the guard rail and near the edge of the space that the rail protects.

A toe board is for situations where workers could be exposed to falling objects from above. OSHA requires a toe board to be 3-1/2 inches or 8.9 cm high from the floor level to the top edge. The board must also handle a force of 50 pounds in any direction.

You'll use a similar method to planning toe boards as what you'd get from guard rails. Measure the areas where you'll require toe boards, and figure out what you'll order from there. You can add toe boards around machines where rolling or wayward items might enter the spot if necessary.

A toe board can cost anywhere from **$1 to $3 per inch**. A six-foot board could go for nearly $100, for example.

The labor cost will vary, although you shouldn't expect to spend too much on it, as the process for installing a toe board will be easier than what works for a guard rail.

A toe board is perfect for businesses with items that can roll on the floor and possibly fall off a surface. The design keeps everything in the workplace organized as well, as you won't struggle to keep things together in one place.

Harnesses

Workplaces where people have to go up and down substantial heights will require those workers to use harnesses. OSHA requires this fall protection in all environments where there's enough height between where the worker may be positioned and the floor.

Harnesses are useful for many situations, including cases where someone has to move up and down a vast room. A harness keeps a person in place and prevents the user from sudden falls while at a height. The most common application for a harness is on a construction or outdoor maintenance project, although such harnesses could be utilized anywhere where there's a sizeable height.

There are three types of harnesses that can work for safety purposes, with each costing a different amount:

1. Body Belt

A body belt is worn around the waist and has a D-ring that can link to a carabiner. The belt can link to a ladder, rope, or another material. A belt can be adjusted to fit one's waist.

A body belt will cost anywhere from $50 to $120 in most situations. The material should be thick enough to stay stable while having enough D-ring spots to make it easy to link to different spots. Make sure when finding a body belt it fits your ladder or anything else you use.

2. Seat Harness

This next option is designed to look like a seat and is best for construction or outside work situations where a person is in a seated position. A belt goes around the waist, while two smaller belts go around the thighs. The leg loops link to the belt through separate straps.

The seat harness keeps the user in a slightly seated position, making it helpful for going up and down a pole, tree, or another tall material. The back or another part should have a D-ring that connects to a carabiner to keep the user connected to a pulley.

Since a seat harness covers more space, it will likely cost from $100 to $150 to purchase. You can order a harness if you plan on going up and down tall materials.

3.   Full Body Harness

A full body harness is vital for people in tall environments. It is helpful for construction workers on the top parts of a building or for a maintenance worker washing windows or other things outside the spot.

A full body harness has a wrap that goes around the waist and over the shoulders. There are also belts around the thighs to create thorough support. There will also be multiple D-rings around the harness to secure the body to a line at many angles.

This harness provides more protection because it supports the whole body. The user has no risk of slipping out of the harness, which is necessary for emergencies.

You can order a full body harness if you have more intensive work needs that require people staying up at high distances for long periods. But expect to spend at least $400 on one of these harnesses.

You can choose which harness you need based on the intensity of the task, the risk the person will be in, and how often you will need to use the harness. Measure the risk your workers will take to determine the appropriate amount of money you will spend on your harnesses.

Nets

Safety nets are necessary for construction sites. OSHA requires safety nets at construction sites with vertical drops of at least six feet.

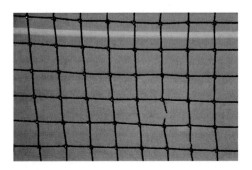

A safety net will collect a person who falls from a distance and keep that person from hitting a hard surface. But the net must be designed to stay safe:

- The fall area must be unobstructed.
- The net must extend outward from the furthest projection of the work surface. If the vertical distance from the working level to the net's horizontal plane is up to 5 feet, the horizontal distance from the outside range of the net from the end of the working surface should be at least 8 feet. The net's horizontal distance increases to 13 feet if the vertical distance is at least 10 feet.
- All nets must be tested after installation, repair, relocation, or after six months if it stays in one place. The test includes a drop test where a 400-pound sand bag is dropped from the highest surface where an employee could potentially fall.

- The net requires an inspection every week. Inspections can occur sooner if anything that might impact its stability occurs.
- The mesh used in the net should have crossings of smaller than 6 by 6 inches.
- The border rope on the net should have a breaking strength of at least 5,000 pounds.
- The connections used for keeping the net spread outward should be less than 6 inches apart each.

Review the site for your safety net to see how large it should be and how you're going to set it up. The fall netting can cost at least $5 per square foot to prepare. A 5 x 10 net could cost about $250 or more to order, for example.

The best safety nets are the pre-made ones that weren't trimmed from previously existing material. The net should be pre-made to specification to help you secure the net well without being hard to prepare yourself.

Most importantly, you have to look carefully at each part of your net during an inspection to ensure there are no cuts. The picture shown above of a safety net features a small cut in one of its parts. While this might sound like a small problem, it could be a sign that there is something wrong with the net. You'd have to check other parts of the net to see how it functions and possibly replace the net altogether.

Getting rid of the net altogether if there are problems and replacing it would be the best idea. Repairing a net might not always work, as it can be tough to tie up loose ends on a net. The work should be planned well to where everything functions right.

Stair and Hand Rails

Stair and hand rails are necessary for stairwells and other places where people may need assistance when walking. A user can handle the rail when climbing up and down a stairwell. The rail can also be used on any islands in the middle of the stairwell.

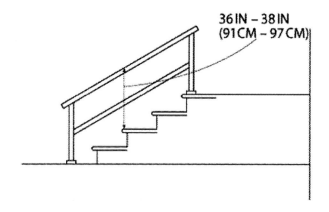

36 IN – 38 IN
(91 CM – 97 CM)

OSHA lists that a hand rail should be 30 to 37 inches or 76 to 94 cm above the stairs. The distance is enough to allow people to grab onto the rail.

Measure the total length of the stairs to determine the approximate length of the rail you need to order. It can cost $30 to $60 per square foot to prepare a hand rail on your stairs. The cost may be higher if you have any unusual patterns or shapes, or if you have any islands midway through the stairwell.

The hand rail is necessary for helping people stay stable while going up and down the stairs. The rail is also essential for older persons who might need extra help moving.

Scaffolds For Construction Workplaces

When was the last time you went by a construction site and noticed a large covering on the ground level? The covering protects people who walk by and allows them to pass without disrupting the construction project. More importantly, those people are protected from any falling items on the spot.

The scaffold also supports the original structure while allowing workers to walk over a space to manage construction tasks.

You will need one of these scaffolds if you plan new construction at your business. OSHA standard 1926.451 reports that a scaffold should support its weight and at least four times the maximum intended load that goes on its body. The planks and other materials should also be spaced well to create a sturdy body.

The best way to get a scaffold for a construction worksite is to rent one from a construction material provider. A construction scaffold can cost anywhere from **$20 to $60 per day to rent**, or you could spend $50 to $150 per week to rent the material.

<u>UK businesses will require a license</u> to acquire a scaffold to use for construction tasks.

The vast size of the scaffold and the extended effort needed to get the scaffold set up makes it where renting a scaffold is ideal. You won't have to store the scaffold anywhere, plus the odds of you requiring it very often won't be substantial after you finish your task.

The scaffold should also have enough support to keep it from moving off a surface or otherwise shifting. The scaffold can move about if wind conditions are too intense or plenty of people are moving around a spot. Sand bags can help keep the scaffolds down, although temporary anchors to the structure can also help. Anything that keeps the scaffold in its place will ensure your scaffolds stay sturdy without risking problems.

Remember when planning your workplace site that you have the necessary fall protection to ensure everyone stays safe. Proper fall protection, whether it involves guard rails or hand rails for the stairwell, is critical for keeping people safe without risking possible harm.

13 Asbestos Removal and Management

How old is your workplace site? Your building might contain asbestos if it was built in the mid-twentieth century.

Asbestos is a dangerous material that will require removal to ensure your workers remain safe. Proper asbestos removal is necessary for keeping your workers from inhaling the compound. Workers who come in consistent contact with asbestos could experience long-term health issues, and these problems could lead to expensive settlements with your business if you're found liable for anything.

The risk of asbestos is dramatic, so getting rid of it or otherwise blocking it off a space will be critical to keeping asbestos fibers from spreading. You will spend money on getting asbestos removed, and you may experience some business disruption in the process. But the long-term costs of not treating asbestos can be dangerous, as you could be liable if someone contracts an illness due to exposure to asbestos.

What Is Asbestos and Why Is It In So Many Workplaces?

Asbestos is a fibrous silicate compound that is naturally occurring. The material is made of flexible fibers that can resist heat, corrosion, and electric shocks.

Asbestos had been popular in construction projects in the early and mid-twentieth centuries. According to the Environmental Protection Agency, asbestos was used as an insulation material. It could be used in ceiling and floor tiles, cement compounds, and various other areas where heat may be prevalent. It could also work in friction products like automobile clutch and brake parts.

The sturdy design of asbestos and its ability to keep heat under control made it an appealing item for construction projects. But the health effects of asbestos have proven to be extremely dangerous to where asbestos is no longer used in new projects.

Asbestos is also part of why demolition projects for old buildings can take a while to complete. A demolition team has to remove the asbestos before starting to keep the fibers from going out in the wild. The demolition crew members also need protection from asbestos, and clearing it before they start working can be vital for keeping everyone safe.

What Makes Asbestos Dangerous?

Asbestos is hazardous to your workers, as people who come in contact with asbestos fibers could inhale or ingest them. These fibers will permanently become trapped in the body, as the body will struggle to break down those parts. The fibers are also very small and can float through the air quickly, making it easier for people to inhale asbestos.

Asbestos fibers are extremely small, as a fiber can be up to 10 micrometers long. This measure is about ten millionths of a meter. The size is small enough to where it cannot be seen by the naked eye.

You also can't see asbestos fibers clumped together without clearing it from a space. The fibers don't have any distinct colors, plus they don't have odors. Most people who are exposed to asbestos may not know there is asbestos in their areas until well after they are diagnosed with a medical condition relating to exposure.

The health effects of prolonged exposure to asbestos can be dangerous:

- A person's risk of lung cancer will be higher when that someone is exposed to asbestos more often.
- Mesothelioma is a rare cancer form that is almost always found in patients who encounter asbestos. Cancerous cells appear in the thin lining around the lung and heart.
- Asbestosis is a non-cancerous condition that can harm the lungs due to asbestos exposure. It can trigger chest pains and breathing difficulties.
- A person's risk of colon cancer or other cancers of the digestive system may also increase.

A chest x-ray or pulmonary function test can help detect asbestos exposure and inhalation in patients.

Initial symptoms of these conditions can appear years after initial asbestos exposure. These problems are often worse among people who have been working in places where asbestos is present more often.

These threats are critical parts of why there are so many restrictions on how asbestos can be used. The import and use of asbestos in the United Kingdom was banned in 1999, and buildings that were built or refurbished after 2000 do not contain asbestos. Meanwhile, Canada's last asbestos mines closed in 2011. But the potential for asbestos to be found in older buildings in any country is still prevalent, as these places used asbestos back before people realized the significant dangers that come with this material.

Where Can Asbestos Be Found In Your Business?

There are many places in your workplace where asbestos can appear. These spaces include:

- Wall and attic insulation
- Roof and side shingles
- Vinyl floor tiles and their backings
- Walls and surfaces near wood-burning stoves
- Patching materials used on walls
- Around oil and coal furnaces

A thorough inspection of your business can help identify where asbestos can appear. A review can check on all these sites, but sometimes asbestos may be found in spots other than these usual areas. A comprehensive check is required, especially if your business site is old enough where asbestos could have been used in the construction process.

How Do You Remove Asbestos?

The risk of asbestos is dramatic, so hiring a professional who can help you remove asbestos from your workplace is critical.

Do not attempt to remove asbestos on your own. You likely won't have the extensive equipment ready to clear it out. The risk of the fibers spreading around your workplace will also be a concern. You could also improperly dispose of the asbestos if you handled it yourself, so asking another party to help you remove your asbestos is the best idea.

The removal team that helps you should be licensed to handle asbestos. The organization that will handle asbestos removal will vary by country. The EPA regulates groups that can remove asbestos in the United States, while the HSE licenses asbestos removal teams in the United Kingdom.

An expert can help you remove asbestos with a few steps:

1. An asbestos removal team can test your property for asbestos.

The test includes a visual inspection of your property. An inspector can remove suspicious materials from the workplace and bring them to a lab for testing. A technician will then check the sample for asbestos.

2. The team will then seal off your workplace.

The removal team will turn off all HVAC units, seal vents, and use plastic sheeting to cover the other areas where the asbestos appears. The spots that will close down will vary surrounding the amount of asbestosis that will require removal. Part of your business could still be functional, but that depends on how much work is necessary.

3. Wet cleanup materials and HEPA filter vacuums will clear the asbestos materials.

The compounds will help bind the asbestos fibers together to keep them from moving out of your property. The vacuum will also ensure the fibers stay in a secure space.

4. Any materials cleared out will stay in a leak-tight container.

The container can be disposed of in a secure location based on local regulations.

5. The asbestos can be recycled for later use.

Asbestos can be recycled into a safe compound. High heat can convert asbestos fibers into a silicate glass. The mixture can be used for other construction processes, as the material is nonhazardous and does not include fibers or other compounds that could be inhaled.

What About Encapsulation?

Asbestos encapsulation is also possible in cases where the asbestos content isn't too significant. A specialist can add a coating around asbestos materials to keep the fibers from becoming airborne. This process protects everyone, but it may not be as effective as complete removal. The protective coating could wear if not treated soon enough, plus any damages to the work environment could cause the area to open and allow the asbestos to leak through and spread everywhere.

What Will You Spend On Asbestos Removal?

The cost to remove asbestos from your business will vary, but you can **expect to spend at least $2,000 to $10,000 on the process.**

Most of the cost to remove asbestos comes from the removal team setting up and sealing your workplace. The process keeps asbestos fibers from spreading, but it can also take a while to complete.

The cost may also be higher if you have more asbestos to remove or the asbestos is in a hard-to-reach spot.

There's also a need to repair surfaces after the asbestos is removed. Sometimes a replacement material will go over the old areas where the asbestos used to be. The repair cost will be separate from the rest of the removal effort.

As for a test, it will cost about $300 to $900 to hire a testing service to check your property at the start.

Cases where encapsulation is recommended will cost less, but not by much. You could spend about 15 to 20 percent less on the service cost if you encapsulate the surface instead of removing anything.

You could choose to encapsulate the asbestos if it is far enough from workers to where it will not pose an immediate threat. Encapsulation also works if the area is sturdy and isn't at risk of tearing apart or being broken into. But removal is still the best idea, as the risk of the asbestos leaking and getting out is still present.

Why Spend Money On Asbestos Removal?

The cost of asbestos removal can be high, but it is necessary to look at this process to ensure your business doesn't waste money on people becoming injured. People who are exposed to asbestos could experience breathing difficulties after a while, making it harder for them to come in to work as necessary. Your business will become less efficient if you don't get enough employees out to work very often.

Also, you won't require workers to wear extensive breathing protection in certain areas after the asbestos is removed. The savings on ordering breathing PPE will be substantial.

The most essential reason to spend money involves how your business could be liable for lung cancer or another long-term health issue if you don't remove your asbestos. A former employee could sue you if that person contracts lung cancer or mesothelioma and your site had enough asbestos.

You are responsible for ensuring your employees remain safe. The Mesothelioma Center writes that an employer must be aware of asbestos in the workplace and provide proper training for people who may be in contact with asbestos. Employers have a duty to protect their employees, and someone could sue you if you did not provide help. You could be named in a person's lawsuit alongside other potentially liable parties like asbestos manufacturers, asbestos mining companies, and the manufacturers of products that contain asbestos.

The amount someone could earn in an asbestos lawsuit could be worth millions of dollars. The costs can come from medical treatments, pain and suffering, lost ability to work, and even possible final expenses. The family members of someone who died from an asbestos-related condition could also sue you for damages if eligible.

Be sure you provide the necessary protection or remove your mesothelioma altogether to ensure you can avoid this threat. The risk of losing immense amounts of money from a lawsuit due to an asbestos-related illness is too dramatic to ignore.

What If You Can't Remove Asbestos?

There might be cases where you cannot remove asbestos. You might not have enough money to remove all the asbestos from an area, for example.

The asbestos may also be in sensitive areas where attempts to clear it out might compromise the structural or functional integrity of your workplace. The repairs for that area after removing the asbestos might be too extensive or otherwise expensive.

You can use a few points to help protect your employees from asbestos exposure:

- A dust mask or respirator is necessary for people who will work around asbestos.
- Protective eyewear also helps, as it keeps fibers from irritating the eyes. While the fibers will not enter the body through the eyes, they can stick in the area and might not be easy to spot until after leaving a site and removing other protective items.
- Disposable coveralls and other protective clothing materials will be necessary to keep asbestos fibers from sticking to one's clothes.
- Signs around an area where asbestos may be present can also help. These signs can inform people to use the proper PPE.

There's also the option to relocate work tasks to other areas. You can check for possible alternate sites for work and see if you can do the same things in those spaces. Relocating work tasks helps when there's enough uncertainty over what might happen, but be sure you know if you can work in a new space. Watch for the cost for getting in that space as well, as it could cost extra for you to relocate some work tasks and devices necessary for the job.

Remember when dealing with asbestos that it can be dangerous and spread anywhere around your workplace. Make sure you are cautious with asbestos and that you remove it soon to keep from risking possible long-term expenses.

14 Lead Paint Removal and Management

Lead paint is another compound that you'll need to remove from your workplace to protect your employees. It is another necessary expense when you consider how much you could save on requiring people to use protective equipment in certain areas. You'll also reduce the risk of being held liable for health issues that came from someone working around lead paint.

Lead paint is easier to spot than asbestos, as there are noticeable visible signs of lead paint peeling and chipping. But the process of clearing it can be tough, as the lead pieces can spread throughout a space. Hiring a professional to help you remove your lead paint and protect your business site well will be ideal for keeping everyone protected and comfortable in the workplace.

Understanding Lead Paint

Lead is a natural element found in the earth's crust. It is denser than other heavy metals.

Lead is often used in various industrial-grade materials like vehicle batteries, radiation protection materials, and weight belts for some machines. Lead is used in these items for having a longer life cycle than other power-holding metals. Its density makes it capable of handling more things, and it works well in reducing radiation exposure from x-rays and other radioactive materials.

But one of the more prominent ways how lead has been used in the past involves lead paint. According to the Centers for Disease Control and Prevention, lead paint had been used in various houses and workplaces before its use was heavily restricted. It was banned from use in homes in the United States in 1978. Lead paint is also illegal for home use in the United Kingdom.

Lead paint is still available in some other countries. While Canadian paint companies have been asked to no longer use lead in consumer paints as of 1990, that request is voluntary. The only law in Canada prohibiting lead-based paints involves how they cannot be used on children's furniture and toys. Lead was also banned from being an additive in paint in Australia in 2010, but it may still be present in trace amounts of up to 0.2 percent.

Lead paint was often used in many workplaces and houses because it dries faster and is more durable than other paint compounds. Lead paint can also resist moisture, so it will maintain its color long enough.

But after a while, the lead paint will start chipping and tearing off the wall. The paint will peel and leave chips and dust around the workplace. You can request a lead paint inspection if you notice any of these signs around your work environment.

The Risk of Lead Paint

People who are exposed to lead paint can experience many side effects. The lead can enter the bloodstream after someone inhales lead, plus it might reach the respiratory system.

Some of the risks of lead paint exposure include:

- Sudden weight loss
- High blood pressure
- Memory loss
- Fatigue
- Headaches
- Constant nausea and dizziness

These problems can harm anyone, but they are especially concerning to children. Kids who encounter lead paint chips could develop breathing or developmental difficulties. It might be harder for the brain to function because lead has entered the bloodstream at high levels. The long-term risk of exposure to lead paint among children will be dangerous.

Removing the lead paint from your business will be essential to protecting everyone in the workplace. In addition to clearing an unsightly image, you'll also ensure lead doesn't spread all around and hurt anyone who comes in contact with it.

Completing An Inspection

You can request a lead paint inspection in your workplace if you notice any paint peeling or cracking around your property. An inspector can review the lead content in your workplace, including in areas where you suspect there is lead paint. The air quality can be tested to identify possible lead contamination.

You could also use a dedicated lead paint testing kit if you want to check for lead paint yourself, but any positive tests will require you to consult a professional for a more thorough analysis. You can test for lead paint by producing a quarter-inch cut through a thick part of the paint and then use a swab from your kit to collect layers of exposed paint. You'll read the swab based on testing instructions to see if there is lead in the paint. The next step is to consult a professional for an inspection if you spot lead.

Think of the testing kit as a preliminary approach to checking for lead paint. The good news is a testing kit is available for about $10 to $15 in most places. The test can provide instant results, as the swab included will be formulated to respond well to lead exposure. You can then move forward with the inspection and the general removal process after you confirm there's a lead problem in the workplace.

How Is Lead Paint Removed?

Lead paint can be removed in one of many ways:

- A wet sanding material can go over the lead paint surface. The sanding compound must include a HEPA filter vacuum that will clear the particles being removed.

- A low-temperature heat gun can also clear off the paint.
- Some removal groups can use hand scrapers to clear the lead paint, but that process will require extra vacuuming help.

No matter what removal process works, a team must clean up all paint chips right away. All floors and other surfaces in the area where the paint was cleared must also be cleaned off and rinsed to ensure there are no lead particles left on the surface.

A vacuum is necessary for removing the lead paint chips. The ventilation systems and openings around a space must also be sealed while using the vacuum to keep those chips from spreading around a spot.

The wall should be bare after the lead paint is gone.

What Does It Cost To Remove Lead Paint?

A typical lead paint removal process can cost from $5,000 to $10,000 in most situations. The rule of thumb is to spend about **$8 to $15 per square foot** to remove the lead. The cost may be higher if the lead paint is in hard-to-reach spots that require additional materials for access.

The cost may be high, but it will be necessary if you're in an older workplace environment where lead paint was used. Lead paint is dangerous and can lead to various physical difficulties if not resolved soon enough. Spending money on lead paint removal can improve workplace efficiency, as health issues will be less prevalent, and people will feel more confident and comfortable in their working environments.

What About the Cost to Repaint a Space?

You can repaint the areas that were treated after the lead paint is removed. The areas will be bare and will require new paint to restore the area and to also protect the wall surfaces.

The cost to repaint your workplace will vary over how many areas require painting and the amount of space needed. A professional painter could charge **$50 to $60 an hour** to repaint the area. The specific number of hours necessary for the work can also vary.

You can talk with a painter about how to repaint the areas where the lead paint used to be for details on what to spend. But no matter what it costs, the painter will paint over the spots with a new material that is safer and will not put your workers or others in the area at risk of harm.

15 Workplace Safety Education Programs and Their Costs

It has never been easier for people to attend workplace safety classes than now. You'll find safety courses at colleges and online learning institutions around the country.

Workplace safety programs can help people what they can do to maintain workplace safety. These include programs prepared by OSHA and other organizations throughout the world.

You can encourage your workers to complete these training courses and other workplace safety education programs. These courses will provide workers the information they need to be safe, plus they don't cost as much money to take as one might expect.

The Most Common Types of OSHA Education Courses

OSHA has multiple education courses for people to complete. These courses will provide employees their official Department of Labor with cards stating they have completed the necessary education programs.

All these programs are available online and through in-person stations at various colleges around the country. People will spend less on online training, although an in-person course might provide more insight into safety standards.

OSHA will also provide all people who complete their courses cards confirming they have completed their studies. These cards encourage people to continue following safe working standards. These cards also will not expire, although the rules for retaking the course may vary by state.

Here are some of the courses OSHA supports:

1.   10-Hour General Course

The 10-hour general industry training course is an entry level course for people wanting to learn about safety standards. The course covers fall protection, ergonomics, hazard communication, electrical functions, emergency action plans, and other basic points people may need to follow.

A 10-hour course will cost about $60 to $100 for each person to complete.

2. 10-Hour Construction Course

There's also a 10-hour OSHA course for construction workers. This course focuses on points more specific to construction workers. These include aspects on PPE, ladders, lead exposure, asbestos exposure, and various other points.
This course also costs $60 to $100 per person.

3. 30-Hour General Course

The 30-hour general industry training course is more specific than the 10-hour one. It incorporates all the aspects of the 10-hour course, plus it includes details on fall protection, bloodborne pathogens, asbestos, machine guarding, welding and cutting, and other technical points.
This course costs $150 to $200 per person.

4. 30-Hour Construction Course

This other construction course is also more detailed than the 10-hour one and also costs $150 to $200 per person. Part of this course includes studying how to manage motorized equipment and vehicles.

5. HAZWOPER Training

HAZWOPER or Hazardous Waste Operations and Emergency Response Standard training is for people who work at sites where hazardous materials are present. The HAZWOPER course is 40 hours and costs $250 on average. An annual eight-hour refresher course to help people maintain certification is also available for $50.

The HAZWOPER program covers aspects on how to handle hazardous materials and using Material Safety Data sheets. Details on how to eliminate these hazards and safeguard people from these compounds will also be covered in a training program.

An Important Note About Testing

All people who take any of these OSHA education courses will have to pass a necessary exam at the end. A person who takes a test three times and fails each time will be locked out of online training and will have to complete an in-person course. The person can no longer take OSHA courses online.

Group Discounts Can Be Available

You may benefit from a group discount when getting more people into these OSHA-approved courses. By enrolling everyone in a course at the same time, you may benefit from a group discount. The discount could be 10 to 30 percent off the regular price of the training program.

The best part about workplace safety courses is they can help people learn all about how to manage different situations that may occur. Colleges and online programs are available today, so look around to see what's open and find a program that helps your workers learn more about the specifics of workplace safety.

Are Renewals Necessary?

Renewal courses for all these OSHA-approved classes are available, and the cost to take a renewal course will be the same as what it costs for the initial one.

Renewal courses are not necessary for many situations. Maritime businesses are the only ones that are required to take renewal courses, as training cards for maritime business employees will expire five years after receipt.

Some states may have rules where you have to renew your training with OSHA every few years. There may be a five-year interval between when you need to take courses, for instance. Check with your state for details on what it requires.

Even if renewal training isn't required, it is still a good idea to go through the process. Renewal training helps you learn about the latest OSHA standards and how to follow them. You could also forget some rules and slip into dangerous habits after a while, so being reminded of OSHA rules always helps.

You'll also encourage workplace safety among your employees if you renew your license. You'll show people the value of safety and encourage them to take OSHA courses themselves. The approach helps everyone stay safe without risking long-term threats or problems.

BritSafe Training

There are also workplace safety programs available in the United Kingdom through the British Safety Council. The council provides courses for BSC certification. These include courses on how to handle various common pieces of equipment, how to handle various chemicals and hazardous items, and fire safety.

BritSafe provides online training for most of its courses, with some courses available to take at one's workplace. The price for completing a training course will vary, but expect to spend at least £25 **plus VAT** on different courses.

CCOHS Courses

Canadian workers can complete various online or classroom-based workplace safety education courses with the Canadian Centre for Occupational Health and Safety. These include courses you can complete at ccohs.ca. You'll spend **at least $49 for each course**, with the options available varying throughout the year.

OSHA's Courses In Australia

OSHA offers workplace safety courses in more than the United States, as you can find OSHA courses in Australia. OSHA provides workplace safety courses through its Australian site at osha.com.au.

Australian courses are WHS-oriented, while there are some specific courses available for people in the mining and construction fields.

Some OSHA courses are face-to-face ones that require in-person training, with many of these courses costing $650 or more to complete over a few days.

Some online programs are also available, and they often cost $100 to $200 less than their in-person counterparts. They are also self-paced courses, which is convenient for workers with busy schedules.

A Diploma of Work Health and Safety course is recommended for people who want to become safety officers or managers in their businesses in Australia. OSHA offers WHS diploma courses for about $2,000 per student. The course includes five in-person classroom days and about 450 hours of total training. Students are expected to complete the course in about 18 months, although it could take as little as six months for some to finish.

16   Lean Principles

The odds are you might have heard about lean operations when looking at ways to keep your business costs down. Lean principles can be used when making your workplace safer.

Lean operations involve refining practices and procedures to keep costs down. You will use fewer resources and steps to complete tasks while producing efficient results. You will do more for your business in less time, plus you will save money because you're not using as many things. There's also the benefit of simplifying your business operations to where you won't waste more time on tasks that aren't necessary for your business.

Lean is necessary for businesses trying to save money and make things more efficient. But it also keeps a workplace safe by simplifying the tasks that require completion. The simplicity of lean principles makes them among the most viable things to explore when boosting workplace performance.

The General Concept of Lean

Lean production or operation involves shortening times and procedures within the business. Lean helps boost response times and provides products or services to customers in less time. More importantly, it also keeps a business from spending as much money as necessary.

Lean is about minimalism, as you're doing more things with fewer resources. You focus on value in your operations and will consistently refine your work efforts to boost that value.

Lean is also about producing little to no waste. Waste in this case entails excessive resources or steps that are not necessary for completing specific tasks.

This practice has become one of the most exciting solutions for workplace efficiency that businesses can use, as it creates a better flow for all current processes while removing excess parts.

Lean operations can incorporate a few steps for enhancing workplace efficiency:

1. Separating parts, tools, and instructions from one another to see what is and isn't necessary for a task
2. Optimizing the items necessary for work
3. Clearing out excess materials that aren't needed
4. Standardization to maintain requirements for work
5. Sustainment operations

The practice helps a business to clear items while producing a sustainable environment for work.

One example of lean processes comes from the car company Toyota. Toyota uses a lean practice that involves the use of machinery with human assistance. Many parts of the manufacturing process are automated, but humans will check the quality of each product to confirm it is made to a standard. Meanwhile, the next step of the manufacturing process only starts when the last step is completed, ensuring there won't be excess work necessary if there's an issue in the assembly line.

The John Deere agricultural company also has a lean practice, as it automates most quality control operations. People can check for defects in new products in less time, allowing the company to produce enough supply to where the company can offer these products to customers at lower prices.

Lean operations provide a simple approach to work that helps a business become more efficient and viable. A business that uses lean functions will have more control over its functions and can succeed well.

How Does Lean Relate to Workplace Safety?

Lean principles are valuable for workplace safety for many reasons. First, lean practices helps remove excess items from the workplace to help ensure you only have the items you need for operations. The risk of various hazards will be reduced because you're using fewer items and moving parts in the workplace. Everything is also cleaner thanks to there being fewer items.

Meanwhile, the workplace will be tidy and simple. People will understand what rules and procedures are necessary. Workers will be less likely to do the wrong things, reducing the risk of injuries and losses. Your workers will also follow a specific schedule that they will follow to prevent themselves from producing waste.

As for your budget, lean will reduce the materials and assets you use. You will not use as many devices or steps to produce items, plus you won't risk workers being idle or spending time doing things they shouldn't be doing. Since your business is more efficient and productive, you won't waste lots of money on assorted unnecessary practices.

How Do You Incorporate Lean Into Your Business?

Identifying Value

The process of incorporating lean into your business safety plan takes a while to complete, but it is about producing a more effective approach to work without spending more money. The first part of incorporating lean involves identifying the value of items in the workplace.

You can review the value of everything in your workplace by looking at the steps you use in a process, the end product, and what the customers will get from the work.

One way to identify value is to review the possible wastes that might come from your processes. Wastes can make work processes more complicated and expensive. They may also make it harder for employees to complete their jobs well enough.

Be sure to check how your business is producing a reasonable value based on:

- **Transportation** – How are people, materials, and equipment moving around? Are they moving more often than necessary?
- **Inventory** – Excess inventory could take up more space and make it harder for you to navigate certain things. The inventory could also create a safety hazard if it obstructs things.
- **Motion** – Excess motions can harm people and equipment. This aspect refers to ergonomic motions and not to transportable items.
- **Waiting** – You might also waste time waiting on things to happen.

- **Overprocessing** – Overprocessing involves doing more than necessary based on what the customer wants, requires, or is willing to spend.
- **Overproduction** – You might also produce more assets than necessary, resulting in excess inventory and additional expenses to handle your items.
- **Defects** – Wasteful processes and excessive actions can result in product or service defects, resulting in lost product. The customer will not want to pay for something if it has defects.

You can use your value definitions to determine what is causing waste in your workplace and figure out ideas on what you want to eliminate. Whether it involves excess items or general steps in the work process, your lean effort can produce a safer and more efficient workplace while keeping your costs down.

Creating a Map Value Stream

Once you figure out the assets in your process and the values of everything your team produces, you can create a map value stream. The stream illustrates the processes you handle and the path everything you produce takes to your customer.

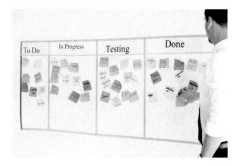

Kanban boards can help review how well your process moves. A Kanban board includes many points listed in three forms:

1. Requested work
2. Work in progress, including items you're working on, what you're waiting for, and what you are reviewing right now
3. Things that are done

You can add multiple Kanban cards in your map value stream, with each card including a listing of the task you want to complete, its deadline, a description of the work, and who will complete the task. You can place this in the proper column based on whether it was requested or is in progress.

You can create multiple swimlanes on your Kanban board to separate different cards among specific teams. One swimlane can be devoted to a specific department, while another could be for urgent tasks you need to manage right away.

This board is perfect for encouraging collaboration. You can also spot work bottlenecks that might limit productivity.

Creating a Flow

After preparing your map value stream, you can produce a work flow that makes it easier for people to prepare tasks. You can achieve this point through your Kanban board.

The Kanban board can help you limit how many works you want to have in progress. You can test working on only a few things at a time. The process can make things run well because more workers are focused on specific tasks, while you will keep previously planned tests from staying in a holding pattern.

Your flow can include a limit on what you can do at a time to keep the workplace safe. Multitasking can be dangerous, as it might lead to defects and could cause injuries or other problems in many environments. Workers might not understand what they have to do and will go all over the place doing many things. They could mix up instructions and cause injuries or other problems that keep the business from staying afloat.

Pull System

The next part of lean for safety involves the creation of a pull system. A pull system involves new work starting only when there's a demand for the work and there is enough capacity for completion. You can generate value that your customers need while avoiding producing excess quantities of something.

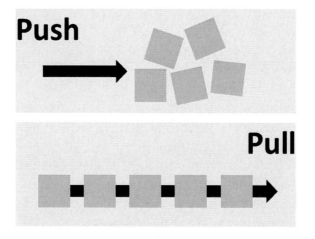

Whereas a traditional work system involves tasks being created and assigned, a pull system involves a task being stored in a queue. Any workers not handling anything will go to the queue and work on tasks that have the highest priority while being ones those people can take.

You can establish steps surrounding when you need to get people to pull tasks. You can establish parameters surrounding when someone will start, plus there can be rules on which tasks are necessary.

The pull system helps you organize all tasks. Instead of everything being up for grabs and hard to reach in some situations, the content in the pull system is easier to use and follow.

Continuous Improvement

One aspect of lean operations to follow in the workplace involves continuous improvement or Kaizen. This aspect of lean work involves making various small changes over time to improve how processes work. The effort adds up over time to create a progressively safer and more responsible workplace.

Kaizen is about looking for the next best opportunities for improvement while making reasonable improvements that will have a greater impact on your business after a while. The work also empowers employees to follow along and suggest further changes as necessary.

The timeframe for continuous improvement can last as long as one needs. Do not expect your lean effort to be completely perfect, as there will always be some opportunity where you could change things around and improve how your business operates. Continuous improvement is necessary for giving your business the help you need.

How Much Will You Save
With Lean Processes?

Lean helps you simplify processes by removing waste and finding new ways to complete projects. It is easier to run your business when you have things organized, plus your workplace will be safer.

Lean management can produce substantial savings in your workplace, although those numbers will vary by situation. A study at Purdue University finds that an average business can reduce labor costs by nearly 30 percent by using lean principles. The reduction comes as less work is necessary for handling tasks. Since fewer things are involved, the work is more efficient and therefore less likely to cause health and safety risks.

There's also a 60 percent decrease in time lost due to issues in the work chain. Whether it involves inventory or excess steps or bottlenecks, work chain issues can keep a business from moving forward. Lean practices simplify the work to where you will complete everything on time while keeping people from rushing and possibly causing injuries.

The Purdue report also finds that extra savings from the work can come from cost avoidance. Since you're reducing the risk of errors and other threats, there's no need to put in extra work to fix problems. The risk of lost productivity and workplace injury claims will also drop because there are fewer assets and steps involved here.

The report also suggests lean practices are intended for long-term savings. While there's a desire to see immediate results, lean is a continuous approach that requires plenty of work and refinement to ensure things work well.

Remember the Four P's

The last thing to see surrounding lean and workplace safety involves the four P's. These points from the <u>Lean Enterprise Institute</u> state that everything in the lean process involves four critical aspects:

1. **Purpose** – Every lean action must have a defined purpose.
2. **Process** – The processes should produce a suitable output or service based on specification. Everything prepared should be based on what you're trying to produce.
3. **People** – The people in your organization should be ready to handle whatever tasks arise.
4. **Performance** – The performance of your work should be efficient and without a problem. For cases where problems arise, you'll need to identify them and understand what can be done to fix these threats.

Lean operations are vital for workplace safety, as they make it easier for your business to grow and succeed while being more efficient. In addition to creating a safer environment with more control over your work, you are also producing an effective work process that helps you move forward while staying safe.

17

Managing Safety Expenses As Tax Deductions

Note: This chapter is about employing tax deductions in the United States. The rules for handling taxes in other countries will vary. Consult a tax professional in your respective area for details on what to expect out of your taxes and how you can potentially reduce your burden.

No business wants to bear with taxes, but it's a fact of life. You'll have to pay taxes on various things your business does, and those taxes can add up after a while. You could spend thousands of dollars on what you earn in some situations.

These taxes will go alongside the costs you're already spending on safety measures in the workplace. But those costs don't have to add more of a burden, as you can control how much you will pay in taxes when you consider how you implement your safety measures.

The expenses associated with creating a safer work environment can be high, but you can keep them under control when you use those expenses as tax deductions.

But a deduction doesn't mean you pay fewer taxes. It means you'll be taxed at a lower amount.

A tax deduction involves a reduction of income that you can be taxed. The deduction occurs due to expenses necessary to bring in extra income and maintain a safe work environment.

The deduction ensures your tax rate will be smaller. Since you have less taxable income after deductions, you won't pay as much on business taxes as usual.

For example, you might have about $60,000 in taxable business income. But you could claim $5,000 in expenses to make your business safer. The claim lets you get a tax deduction of $5,000, meaning you will have $55,000 in taxable business income afterward.

By reducing that income, you are also trimming your tax expenses. It becomes easier for you to manage your taxes this way, as your burden becomes less substantial.

But you must also watch what you're doing when getting a tax deduction through your safety expenses. IRS Publication 535 provides details on what you can claim.

Publication 535 states you can claim tax deductions on things like these:

- The cost of raw materials and products necessary for maintaining workplace safety
- Business assets, including land, buildings, machines, vehicles, and other items of value
- Improvements that cover recurring activities in the workplace, including ones that will be conducted more than once after starting your service
- Improvements that come from the use of the property in your business
- Any actions that keep your property functional and efficient
- Costs incurred during the improvement process, including labor expenses

These deductions can add up and keep your tax burden under control. But you'll also have to keep proper records on all your expenses when getting your safety improvements ready.

Keeping records on what you spend and how you're implementing those plans is essential to helping you go forward and complete your work without worrying about spending too much in the long term.

How Much Can You Deduct From Your Taxes?

The amount of money you can deduct from your taxes through measures to enhance workplace safety will vary surrounding your situation. The general expenses for workplace safety needs can be deducted in most situations, but there may be rules over what constitutes a deduction.

There are a few rules from the IRS based on Publication 535 surrounding how much you can deduct:

- Deductions can be used if the efforts are for active procedures.
- You will not be able to deduct any losses from safety management efforts that do not work or are scrapped.
- Some activities may be interpreted as indirect deductions. You could deduct a percentage of an expense equal to the percentage of the workplace that you use for business purposes.
- Interest expenses can be deducted if you take out a loan to pay for your safety improvements.
- Travel expenses could also be deducted if they are relevant to workplace safety. These include the costs necessary to travel to acquire whatever goods you want to use.

- Fees from professional services necessary to workplace safety can also be deducted as business expenses.

Be sure when looking at your business expenses that you have an idea of what you can deduct. Tax deductions make it easier for you to plan your workplace safety efforts, as you know you can keep from spending more on your taxes.

But be cautious when looking at how your tax deductions work. You can consult a tax expert for assistance in helping you see how well your deductions can fit your needs.

18 Using Tax Incentives For Handicap Accessibility

Some of the most prominent tax incentives you can enjoy when maintaining a safe workplace involve tax benefits for meeting handicap accessibility compliance standards.

Most of these incentives are available to businesses in the United States. The Americans with Disabilities Act was formed in the United States to prohibit discrimination based on a person's disability. The ADA requires businesses to provide reasonable accommodations to employees and others who are disabled. The ADA also imposes accessibility requirements for public spaces.

You can make your business handicap-accessible to ensure everyone is capable of reaching different assets around your workplace. Many of the reasonable accommodations you'll need to prepare for your workplace are simple and won't cost much money to handle. There's also a potential for you to earn tax incentives when you're compliant, making it easier for you to maintain workplace safety without losing lots of money.

You'll have to provide enough reasonable accommodations to benefit from tax incentives regardless of the country you live in. Reasonable accommodations are adjustments made within a system to accommodate people with certain needs. The effort is about allowing a business to be fair to everyone while providing a simple approach to supporting worker and customer needs.

Some of the reasonable accommodations you can incorporate include these:

- Provide multiple measures for how you can communicate with people. These include written documents for people who might struggle with hearing, or audio-based content for people with poor vision.
- Provide more accessible spaces around the workplace, including ramps for wheelchair use and minimal curbs and barriers that require extra effort for a wheelchair to go over. Rails and other items for people who need help moving around a space can also work.
- Adjust products, devices, or other items to make them more accessible in some environments.
- Adjust transportation services to make them easier for people to access. These include wheelchair ramps for people and hand controls for those who cannot control a traditional vehicle.
- Reassignment can also help, as an employee can be reassigned to a different position if that person cannot perform the essential tasks necessary

in one's job. This accommodation is affordable because you don't have to create a new position or transfer any other employees.

The cost of getting your business to comply with needs for handicapped people will vary. You could spend thousands of dollars on an audit to help review how well your business meets handicap standards. This charge goes alongside any expenses necessary to become compliant.

Claiming Your Tax Benefit In the United States

The IRS Code allows businesses to earn tax deductions for becoming ADA-compliant. Section 44 illustrates this point for small businesses, while Section 190 is for all businesses.

Architectural or Transportation Tax Deduction

The first ADA tax benefit available is for all businesses. The architectural or transportation tax deduction is for covering the removal of various barriers in the workplace, whether it involves building ramps, widening entry points, adjusting vehicles, and anything else of value.

You can use Publication 535, Business Expenses to determine which ADA-related expenses can be claimed as tax deductions. You can deduct up to $15,000 from your expenses, making it easier for you to cover these costs.

Small Business Tax Credit

The other ADA tax benefit is the small business tax credit through IRS Form 8826. This form is for small businesses that have spent money to comply with ADA rules.

The tax credit covers 50 percent of expenses from $250 to $10,250. The maximum amount you can get from this credit is $5,000.

This credit is only for entities that qualify as small businesses. A small business is defined as a business with 30 or fewer full-time employees or a company with $1 million or less in gross receipts in the past year.

What About Your Website?

You can also earn a tax credit if your business has an ADA-compliant website. Your website will need to be programmed to be accessible to all people.

Some of the reasonable accommodations you can use to make your website accessible to everyone include:

- Multiple font size options for people who are hard of seeing
- Captioning for videos and other multimedia content
- Reader programs that digitally read the word content on a site
- Color options for people with sight or colorblindness issues

These features are convenient for everyone, but these don't have anything to do with workplace safety. But they do help you save money by helping you get a tax credit that can keep your expenses down.

You can also use the principles for creating an accessible website in helping you find ideas for creating an accessible worksite. You may be inspired to consider more signage or digital devices that can help guide people through different areas. You've got plenty of ways to make your worksite safe and accessible, so take some inspirations from your web design plan to see what might fit your business plan.

UK Tax Advantage

The process of saving money on taxes in the United Kingdom is different, as you don't have to report equipment or services necessary to allow disabled employees to do their work. You don't have to provide the HMRC with data, and you won't have to pay tax or National Insurance on anything necessary for accessibility purposes.

You must offer the same accessibility materials to all people who may become disabled. Fair access is necessary for ensuring everyone receives the accessible materials they require for any purpose.

Those who provide equipment or services to handicapped people or provide accessible workplace functions in a salary sacrifice arrangement will not be eligible for tax exemptions. You'll have to complete Form P11D for your taxes and report the salary the workers are giving up and the cost of the items necessary for making your workplace accessible.

19

Outsourcing and Freelancers

Take a quick look at how your current workplace is arranged. How many people are working in your business? Are there too many in your space right now?

More importantly, does your business require you to handle all the people who are there right now? Some workers might be doing things in your workplace that aren't necessary. They might be doing menial tasks that can be handled elsewhere, or those people are idle and are wasting your payroll.

An excess number of workers might make you spend more on payroll than necessary. But too many people can also increase the risk of workplace injuries. Between people getting in the way of one another and constantly interfering with each other's operations, it can be tough to run a business if you have too many bodies in one spot.

But there's a way how you can resolve this common problem. You can use outsourcing to help you fill positions that can cost less to hire than regular in-person employees. You can outsource various projects in your workplace to different freelancers who can manage many tasks.

What does outsourcing your work to freelancers have to do for workplace safety?

It's a safe option because there won't be as many people in your office as expected. Your liability for workplace injuries will be reduced, as your outsourced talent will work elsewhere.

Outsourcing is a useful practice that is being used by various companies. A 2020 study from Deloitte found that nearly 60 percent of global companies use outsourcing to manage various tasks. A majority of those companies use outsourcing to save money, but they also do this to keep their businesses more flexible while bringing products or services out to market faster.

The Deloitte study also finds that outsourcing can be a valuable alternative to robotic process automation. While the idea of using automated machines to complete tasks sounds appealing, the cost of bringing in such machines can be cost-prohibitive. It's also hard to create smart enough bots that can complete tasks the right way. Outsourcing work to actual people can be a more effective solution when managing workplace tasks.

What Does a Freelancer Do
For Your Business?

A freelancer is a person you will outsource your work to. The freelancer may work for you, but you are not that person's main boss. A freelancer works for themselves and is self-employed. That person can take contracts from companies like yours to complete whatever tasks you wish to outsource.

A freelancer will set one's own work hours and keep track of the time one spends on various work tasks. That person can bill clients for the work one provides.

You can provide instructions to a freelancer about what you want that person to do. But you cannot control when the person works, where that person works, or whatever methods someone might prefer using. A freelancer may also work for multiple employers at a time, so that person is not going to work exclusively for you like a regular employee.

Are Freelancers Employees?

The freelancers you hire are not official employees at your workplace. They are contract workers who provide services to you based on agreements.

So how does this relate to saving money?

Since your freelancer is not an employee, you won't be responsible for many of the expenses you'd spend on your existing workers. You do not have to pay for a freelancer's health insurance, vacation time, 401(k) matches or other retirement benefits, or anything else the worker might get if that person was an employee.

Employees go on your business payroll, which can be limited at times. Your payroll would withhold necessary taxes like income and Social Security taxes. The employees will also be entitled to whatever benefits are available. These benefits are necessary for helping you keep your employees.

But since your freelancer isn't an official employee, you don't have to provide all those things that that worker. A freelancer can move on to different clients as necessary. Freelancers often have various duties they want to cover and will complete their tasks in different ways.

The freelancer you hire is responsible for one's own insurance. The freelancer is also responsible for managing taxes, including self-employment taxes. That person will also pay for their other benefits separately from you. The health insurance policy a freelancer has can be completely different from what you provide, for instance.

Onboarding and Training Efforts

You can also save money with freelancers because you won't have to train such a person as much as you'd do for an official employee. Traditional employees require plenty of onboarding and training work to understand everything necessary for handling their jobs. You could spend lots of money on training these people, and that expense can become worse if you have a substantial turnover.

Freelancers won't have to undergo all those onboarding and training processes. Since the freelancer's services focus on a very specific aspect of work, you don't have to provide that person as much info as others who would be on your site. The only details you have to provide are the ones necessary for the task at hand.

The freelancer doesn't have to study your company culture or whatever goals you have. The freelancer may not be emotionally attached to your business, so teaching that person about everything in your workplace may not be the most productive or sensible idea for work.

How Do You Hire a Freelancer?

One benefit of a freelancer is that the person works as a service. You will only hire that person when necessary.

You can use a few steps to hire a freelancer:

1. Figure out the scope of your work.

Be specific when determining the kind of work your freelancer will complete. You can explain particulars on what your freelancer will do, what the person will use, and any targeted audiences the freelancer will support.

Make sure you explain what skills you're looking for in a job so the freelancer won't ask too many questions. You can discuss specific needs you might have if you wish.

2. Review how much you're going to pay the freelancer for the work.

You can choose how much you're going to pay your freelancers for all the tasks they will complete. You might charge a specific amount based on where a person is located and how much experience you need out of someone.

Check around to see similar freelancer postings involving your field to see what people are charging. Sometimes the freelancer cost will be lower than what you'd spend on a regular employee's work, but in other cases the worker might ask for more money.

Since the freelancer pays one's taxes and runs one's own business, you might have to pay that freelancer more money. But the fact you're not paying for insurance or other benefits could still keep you from spending as much overall as you would a regular employee.

3. Go to different freelancer platforms to find someone of use.

You've got a thorough array of freelance platforms to explore when hiring someone. Websites like Fiverr, Upwork, Freelancer.com, Flexjobs, Toptal, SimplyHired, and Jooble are all good choices to consider.

You can set up an account with any of these platforms and use it to find details on different freelancers available for hire. You can read their profiles, ratings, and reviews. Many workers will also provide portfolios showing previous works they've done for others.

Be advised that these platforms will charge you money to find someone. Fiverr charges a 5.5 percent service fee for tasks, while Freelancer.com charges a 3 percent fee for fixed-price and hourly jobs.

Some places may also specialize in offering freelancers in very specific fields. While a website like Freelancer.com can offer freelancers in all fields, some may concentrate on one group. 99designs is a website that exclusively offers freelance graphic designers, for example.

4. You can also use social media platforms to find freelancers.

There are many freelance groups available on social media platforms as well. Facebook and LinkedIn are both places that host groups of freelancers searching for jobs. You can learn about different freelancers through these platforms and directly reach out to them for help. This effort takes an extra bit of time to manage, as you'd have to search around these platforms yourself to find someone. But you won't have to spend extra on service fees like what other platforms charge, so you'll still save money.

5. You can contact a freelancer that might interest you.

The next step is to contact the person you want to hire for a task. You can check on many things surrounding whoever you want to consult:

- The person's experience
- Prior samples of work
- Whether that person has completed tasks similar to yours
- How that person completes work
- The amount of work your candidate has outside of what you have
- General philosophies of what one wants out of a task
- Reviews from other people surrounding that person's work

You can schedule an interview with the freelancer and maybe request that person complete a test of one's skills. Make sure the analysis is efficient and doesn't take too much time, as you might need to get that someone ready to work for you soon.

1. Figure out how you're going to hire the freelancer.

Deciding to hire a freelancer for a task is easy. It's figuring out what the freelancer will receive that's a challenge. You don't want the freelancer to know too much about what you're doing, as giving out too much information can be risky. That person might share that data with others, whether intentionally or accidentally.

The best way to hire a freelancer is to provide the necessary details and materials for completing a job. Don't give that person anything outside of whatever is necessary for the work at hand.

You can also request the person fills out a non-disclosure agreement or NDA. An NDA is a legally binding document that lists confidential data you will share with other parties. The NDA will state that the worker cannot share the secret contents with other parties, including during and after the employment period.

The NDA protects you from losses, as you can sue a freelancer who breaks an NDA if that break leads to financial damages and legal expenses.

Remember to be prompt when trying to hire someone. Freelancers might be choosy over where they will go, with some of them attempting to flock to higher-paying jobs. Others who are in high-demand will also be hard to find, so you might be stuck looking for newer freelancers who might not be as useful. But sometimes these freelancers might be willing to work a little harder to prove themselves.

2. After the freelancer starts working, you can stay in touch with that person and confirm one's ability to complete different tasks.

You can complete a thorough review of everything your freelancer produces over time to ensure that someone is working well. Your freelancer will ensure one's work is perfect and suitable, as that person won't be paid unless their work is good enough by your standards. Many freelancers may be more proficient in their work for you, but it's essential to see how well a freelancer can serve your needs when finding someone to hire.

Paying Your Freelancer

The cost of hiring a freelancer can be cheaper than what you'd spend to hire someone to work in your business as a permanent employee. Since you're saving money on benefits, it's possible to pay less.

But it's also essential to see how much money you will spend. One idea to help you see what you'd spend on a freelancer is to consider what other people are spending on freelancers for jobs similar to what you have. You can look around online to see what's open to getting a general frame for what you'd spend.

Three Pricing Options

One idea for paying a freelancer is to pay that person based on one of three pricing options:

1. An hourly or daily rate; this point works if you have specific work needs for your freelancer
2. A fixed rate for the project; this option is based on the value of the project and will guarantee a specific amount to the client
3. Retainer, or a weekly or monthly charge where you guarantee a freelancer's services; you'll discuss the work the person completes first

Allowing the Freelancer To Set One's Rate

You can also allow the freelancer to set one's rate for how much that person will earn on work. The freelancer can list a specific rate based on many factors:

- Income tax one might spend
- How long it would take for that person to complete a task
- Any expenses one might incur
- General living costs

A freelancer will often prepare one's rate based on experience and general financial needs. One calculation a freelancer can use is a Minimum Acceptable Rate or MAR, the lowest hourly rate one is willing to work.

The MAR is a suitable starting point for freelancers to use when proposing their salaries. The MAR is a calculation of the living costs someone has, the overhead business costs, and the salary all divided by the hours worked each year with the tax added.

The MAR allows the freelancer to use a profit margin to dictate how much one would have to earn to reach that rate.

Country Standards

One exciting part of paying freelancers is that many operate from different parts of the world. Some freelancers may be willing to work for less because the cost of living in these areas is lower than in other places.

Fiverr writes that some countries have extremely low costs of living. The cost of living in Thailand, Albania, New

Zealand, and Hong Kong is cheaper than in the United States and Canada. People in these countries might request less money than expected, making them more affordable to hire.

But the international nature of those employees makes it more essential for you to review how well they can handle your tasks. Proper communication is also essential because although English is a prominent language in many of these countries, that doesn't mean every person in those areas speaks English as their first language.

People who live in high-income areas where the cost of living is higher will charge more. These include workers in cities like Sydney, Chicago, London, and Toronto.

How Many Years of Experience?

More experienced freelancers will typically charge more money than others. Whether it's you or the freelancer dictating that price, be ready to pay more for someone with more work under one's belt.

There are three levels of experience you can consider for a freelancer:

1. **Junior** – A junior freelancer will have less than three years of experience.
2. **Standard** – A standard freelancer will have worked for at least three years in one's field.
3. **Expert** – An expert will have at least ten years of experience. You can widen your search for someone with seven years of experience.

You can adjust how much you'll pay for a freelancer based on one's experience. An expert could get at least twice as much money from one's work as a junior freelancer.

The more experienced freelancers will ask for more money because they have done more and are looking for further compensation. The payments someone might request can be high, but they will have enough experience and knowledge in their fields to where that is justified.

How Do You Pay a Freelancer?

The process of paying a freelancer is flexible, as you've got many options to explore when paying a freelancer for one's services.

You can use one of many payment options, but be aware of some of the charges associated with paying a freelancer. You'll need to look for something that fits without having you spend more money on charges:

1. Paper checks

You can use paper checks to pay a freelancer without paying extra charges. It can take a few days or weeks to get a paper check out to your client, plus it might take a while for someone to cash one's check. Make sure you use a reasonable effort for getting a paper check ready.

2. PayPal

PayPal is a popular solution for paying freelancers, as PayPal offers an electronic platform where you can move funds to another person. PayPal offers automated currency exchanges, plus it is free to send money through a bank transfer or a PayPal balance. The freelancer can also transfer the funds one earns to one's bank account or anything else linked to the PayPal account.

You will spend extra if you use a credit or debit card to send a payment to your freelancer through PayPal. A 2.9 percent transaction fee will apply in this case.

3. Escrow service through a freelance platform

Many freelance platforms also offer escrow services where you can complete payments. An escrow payment involves a third party receiving and sending money to another person with the transfer, depending on the conditions the two parties agreed to use. This process is simple and convenient, but it may cost extra to use it depending on where you go.

4. EFT

An electronic fund transfer or EFT is a payment that doesn't require a check or online payment system. An EFT is an electronic transfer of money from one bank account to another. It works without bank staff having to intervene and handle the payment.

EFT payments can work between multiple accounts. These can work even if the two parties have accounts with different banks.

EFT payments are helpful, but it does cost money to get them ready. You might spend a monthly fee with your bank for access to EFT payments, or you might pay a percentage of the total transaction for each transfer you complete.

☐ VOID ☐ CORRECTED			
PAYER'S name, street address, city or town, state or province, country, ZIP or foreign postal code, and telephone no.	1 Rents $	OMB No. 1545-0115	Miscellaneous Information
	2 Royalties $	Form **1099-MISC** (Rev. January 2022) For calendar year 20___	
	3 Other income $	4 Federal income tax withheld $	Copy 1
PAYER'S TIN	RECIPIENT'S TIN	5 Fishing boat proceeds $	6 Medical and health care payments $	For State Tax Department
RECIPIENT'S name	7 Payer made direct sales totaling $5,000 or more of consumer products to recipient for resale ☐	8 Substitute payments in lieu of dividends or interest $	
Street address (including apt. no.)	9 Crop insurance proceeds $	10 Gross proceeds paid to an attorney $	
City or town, state or province, country, and ZIP or foreign postal code	11 Fish purchased for resale $	12 Section 409A deferrals $	
	13 FATCA filing requirement ☐	14 Excess golden parachute payments $	15 Nonqualified deferred compensation $	
Account number (see instructions)	16 State tax withheld $ $	17 State/Payer's state no.	18 State income $ $

Form **1099-MISC** (Rev. 1-2022)   www.irs.gov/Form1099MISC   Department of the Treasury - Internal Revenue Service

What About Taxes?

In the United States, you will handle freelancer taxes through a 1099 form. This form involves miscellaneous income a person collects. It documents payments a person receives from a party that doesn't typically work as a regular employer. You will fill out a 1099 form with the proper details and then send a copy to the freelancer and another to the IRS. The 1099 form is different from the W-2 a regular employee would receive.

Other equivalent forms to file include the following:

- Canada: T4A
- United Kingdom: P60; a person gets a separate P60 for each job one completes
- Australia: No specific form, but Australian freelancers must claim income on one's tax return

Another method of paying a freelancer involves paying for one's work based on different milestones. This measure involves paying someone when that person completes specific objectives. For example, you might pay someone half the money you are promising if that person is halfway through the work and you are satisfied with the task.

Paying people based on milestones is smart, as it encourages the worker to keep putting in an effort. The worker will also know you're committed to completing a payment, as you can show you're going to pay someone at some point during the work.

You'll have to provide a schedule of payments before the freelancer starts working, plus you'll have to review how the work is going. You can check the work to confirm the freelancer is working right and everything is going well. The freelancer will also feel motivated after hearing you like the work so far.

But watch for how well the worker continues the task after paying for a milestone. The worker should continue to manage your project and get it ready soon enough.

The problem is that sometimes a worker might not do as well late in the task as one did at the beginning. Burnout or stress might be problems that make it harder for the worker to finish these tasks.

But at the same time, a worker who is paid by milestones may want to keep working because you're ready to make payments. You should still watch for what could happen if a worker doesn't handle the tasks you assign as well.

What About Deposits At the Start?

The last thing to see for hiring a freelancer involves completing a deposit when you start working with someone. A freelancer can record a deposit worth a specific amount before starting, as the freelancer wants to ensure you have a plan for paying that person.

You can establish a deal where you'll pay the freelancer about 10 to 20 percent of whatever you will pay that person. The freelancer will note you have the capability of paying someone, and that person will start working with the goal of earning the rest of the money.

Be advised that you won't be able to get this deposit back from the worker if you aren't satisfied with that person's effort. You won't pay for the rest of the work if it doesn't fit your standard, but you'll still be out of that small portion. Plan how much you're willing to risk on the freelancer before you start so you don't spend more on someone that might end up not being as effective as you wish.

20 Safety Initiatives

Workplace safety can work in many ways, but it will only be effective if you get enough people on board to support whatever plans you want to use. You can use many safety initiatives in the workplace that will help people get on board. Best of all, these safety plans won't cost more money to use than you might expect.

Planning safety initiatives can help your business thrive and succeed while going forward with unique plans for the operation. These initiatives can also establish a caring culture in your business. The odds of workers missing time or trying to work while not in their best conditions will also be minimal, as you're encouraging a rational and responsible work environment.

Contagion Mitigation

Disease outbreaks can occur in many forms. These include outbreaks involving respiratory diseases and bacterial infections. Measles outbreaks, hepatitis outbreaks, and salmonella and listeria infections are among the most common threats you might find today.

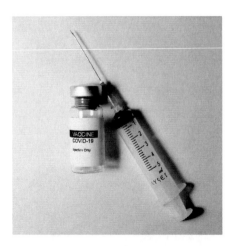

The CDC has a thorough listing of outbreaks in the United States and elsewhere. Details on such outbreaks are always evolving, as new problems will often arise.

One safety initiative you can use at your workplace entails finding ways to prevent contagions from occurring. You can create a contagion mitigation plan that doesn't cost much money to manage.

You can do the following in your contagion mitigation initiative:

- Offer a vaccine campaign where people are encouraged to get vaccines for various seasonal illnesses. On-site vaccine administrations can be provided for free through various healthcare providers.
- You can also expand or update your sick leave policy to cover possible infectious diseases.
- Hand hygiene training will help people learn how to wash well to keep illnesses from spreading.
- Sick family member leave can also be made available. A worker can tend to a sick family member, and the worker can be allowed to stay at home to care for that person without risking spreading an illness elsewhere.
- A ventilation system review can help see how well the air in your workplace functions.
- You could also train people on how to use remote communication tools for situations where they cannot physically make it to your workplace.

These workplace measures are free or low-cost and will encourage workers to be more responsible and careful. They will not risk spreading illnesses to other places, ensuring your workplace remains more efficient.

Your employees may feel encouraged to maintain health and safety measures these ways, especially as vaccines for various illnesses are becoming more important than ever. But you must put in your own effort to get people to take that next step and get vaccinated and follow various safety measures.

Hazard Identification and Prevention

Another workplace initiative you can plan involves how to spot hazards. You can create a safety program where you'll help people review potential hazards throughout the workplace.

Your program can include helping people understand how to read different warning signs or how to spot situations where something looks unusual or amiss. Some of the safety points you can help your workers learn about include:

- Slip and fall hazards
- Electrical hazards
- Signs of a utility leak
- Ergonomic issues
- Signs a machine or device is not working well
- Housekeeping points workers can handle
- Biological hazards, including whether something is poisonous or contagious

People can learn about how to spot these hazards and manage them. Anyone can learn about these points to prevent further harm in the workplace.

Reviewing Your Control Measures

You won't have to spend money to review whatever control measures are in your workplace. You can create a plan where certain employees are responsible for handling safety concerns and preventing problems from occurring.

You can talk with employees closest to the risks you need to control. Your discussion can include:

- Seeing what control measures are necessary
- Whether your current control methods are causing new problems
- Any legislation that might change how well your control measures are working
- Whether everyone is up-to-date on their training

After figuring out the answers to these points, you can use a few steps to improve how well the control measures can work:

1. Assign certain workers to specific safety-related tasks.

Each worker you assign a task to should review the work and monitor all safety measures to ensure they fit the business well. The plan can encourage accountability among your workers.

2. Establish a system for how people will communicate with each other.

Allow people to communicate with each other and yourself through whatever means you prefer. Whether through meetings, messages you post, or even social media, proper communication will help all control measures stay functional.

3. Consult each worker and see if they are current on training.

Provide the necessary educational materials to your workers based on what they need to manage.

4. Stay updated on new trends.

Whether it involves new technologies or measures for handling workplace safety, make sure everyone knows what's happening in the field and that you know what works.

Encouraging Workplace Safety Participation

As helpful as a workplace safety program can be, it's not always easy to get people to want to stick around. You'll have to motivate your workers to where they'll want to follow your safety plan.

The best way to encourage workplace safety participation is to use positive reinforcement. Thanking your workers for being safe and following the rules can make a positive impact, as those workers will know you're paying attention to their work. They will want to keep on being safe and following the rules, as they know you'll be happy with their work when managed well.

You can also inform your workers about the ownership they have in workplace safety efforts. Let people know how their actions will make a positive impact on how the workplace functions.

You could even offer incentives to encourage people to work safely. You could provide rewards to your employees based on how they maintain workplace safety.

The employees in your workplace are essential to providing a safe and secure environment where everyone can feel confident in how well they can work. Be sure when getting your workplace ready that everyone feels confident in what is around and that there's no need to worry about whatever might happen in the workplace.

21 Annual Reviews

The measures you put into keeping your workplace safe are critical for success. Regular measures of how well you're keeping your employees and other people safe can help you see if you're doing things right or if you need to fix things in some way.

An annual review will help you see how well your business is staying safe. You can review how well your employees are working and identify possible issues involved.

Your annual safety review can help you see how your business works and if you're spending the right amount of money to keep everyone protected. You can review your business based on incidents reports and any long-term issues stemming from whatever happens.

Your safety report can include details on your business operations and what makes your company function well. You can see if your workers are paying attention to your work tasks, plus workers need to see if they're doing things right or wrong.

Most importantly, you can reinforce your safety protocols to your workers during your annual review. You can remind workers about what they should be doing and how they can keep their work efforts under control.

What Goes Into a Workplace Safety Review?

Your workplace safety review can include multiple steps:

1. Review injury reports from the past year.

See what injuries were reported in the workplace in the prior year. How many people were injured, and how were they injured? Were these injuries severe, and did people lose time in the workplace due to these injuries?

Check on what happened to your workers to see if there are any noticeable trends. You might spot cases where multiple people were injured the same way or around the same time. Sometimes a trend might occur because of a change in the workplace, or that trend ended because you made some corrective measure to your work.

2. Look at your current safety measures.

Compare the safety measures you are implanting with any injury reports you have. Are your current safety measures covering cases where these injuries might happen, or are there noticeable gaps in how you're managing these injuries? Your analysis can help you spot whether your measures are suitable enough.

3. Check on any changes you made to your safety plans.

You might have made some changes to your safety plans due to new devices or processes being introduced in the workplace. Some laws might have also required you to make changes in how you work. Whatever the case, you can review your work and see if the changes you made impacted your injury reports.

4. Look at your current budget for safety functions.

Your safety budget should be reasonable, but it should also be kept under control, especially as inflation becomes a threat worldwide. Your safety budget can include multiple points for operating your business and how you're going to serve people.

Everything you put into your annual review can help you see what you're doing when helping you find opportunities for how you're going to improve upon your current safety measures.

Conclusion

Workplace safety is essential for every business. You must provide a safe environment where your workers will feel confident while on the job. The space should be protected and arranged to where no one will be at risk of harm.

But you should also watch how much money you're spending on your safety measures. The points in this guide will help you see how you can create a safer workplace while avoiding excess costs.

Be sure to review the points in this guide to see how your business can stay safe. Whether it entails freelancing or lean work or anything else you can add, you'll find many ways to stay safe and support your business functions.

Good luck in your efforts to keep your business safe while keeping costs down. You'll find the measures in this guide to work well for your worksite.

Made in United States
North Haven, CT
08 January 2023

30792257R00137